# THE 12 STEP

# MIND-BODY-FOOD
# RESET

# THE 12 STEP MIND-BODY-FOOD RESET

*Jessica* **SEPEL**

Pan Macmillan Australia

# Contents

**7**

Manage your stress so it doesn't manage you *127*

**8**

Spend 20 minutes making dinner. That's it! *141*

**9**

Combat sugar cravings, for life *171*

**10**

Focus on your health, not your weight *193*

**11**

Indulge moderately, without guilt! *207*

**12**

Finally, remember that there are no rules *229*

# I haven't shared this story before ...

When I was just seven years old, I was enjoying a family holiday in Plettenberg Bay, a gorgeous coastal town in South Africa (where I grew up). We had a beach house there, and it was my haven. My sisters and I spent our days swimming, bike riding, hiking, cooking, eating and running around in our bikinis.

It was a magical time in our lives, and I felt so free.

I remember standing on the balcony in my bikini. I can still smell the ocean breeze. I looked down at my stomach and felt unhappy about it. It was the first time I'd ever connected with my body in a negative way. I just remember thinking that it was bloated and big. (It's important to keep in mind that I was always a tall and slender girl. I was never overweight.)

I rushed to the mirror to look at my stomach and spent 15 minutes criticising it, and trying to suck it in. I can see the bathroom and my bright pink bikini so clearly in my mind now – that's how much this memory has stuck with me.

This is one of my first, and most powerful, memories, and this moment would affect my relationship with my body for the rest of my childhood and teens. I didn't like what I saw in the mirror that day. It was the first mirror fight I'd have. Thousands more would follow.

I went up to a family member and asked, 'Is my stomach fat?'

I stood there waiting for her answer. Hoping, wishing she would tell me I was being silly.

She said, 'Yes, it is a little fat and chubby. It's cute. Don't worry!'

But all I heard was the word **fat**.

I was absolutely crushed.

I felt so confused. I didn't understand what she was saying or why she was saying it. I still don't.

I knew I wasn't fat, but her comment made me question that. It gave me anxiety – a feeling I'd truly never experienced before that moment. To this day, if I'm having negative thoughts about my body, that same feeling pops up.

Unfortunately, her response was the worst thing she could have said to me at that young, impressionable age. Sadly, I think it damaged my body image and caused me to idealise 'skinny' for a long time. It prompted the battle I had with my body for years. This exchange also made me feel that my family member disapproved of me. Looking back, this incident probably sent me into the spiral of feeling like I wasn't 'enough'. It marked the beginning of my obsession with needing to be thin to be loved and accepted.

I haven't shared this story before …

I remember responding with something along the lines of, 'How can I get a flatter stomach?' or, 'Can I go on a diet to flatten my stomach?'

I was seven!

And the saddest part? To this day, I lift up my shirt in the mirror and look at my stomach with dissatisfaction. Seven-year-old Jess is still there, desperate to know she's good enough.

I know that my family member didn't mean to cause harm. She couldn't have imagined the impact her words would have on me. This is one of the reasons I always ask parents to avoid commenting on their child's weight or size. It can have long-lasting effects.

Thankfully, I now have the tools to manage my health and my thoughts. I spent far too many years flailing around without them – trying one fad diet after another. I'm so grateful for my journey, and that I got the support I needed to shed the negative thoughts and behaviours that burdened me for so long. Now I want to share those tools with as many people as possible so they can enjoy the same freedom I experience when I eat, exercise and move through the world.

That's why I started my business and why I've written this book.

# Challenge your beliefs, change your life

Our belief systems affect so many aspects of our lives without us even realising it, including our relationship with food and our body. I don't want you to blame yourself, though. Sometimes, our beliefs stem from childhood – how we were raised, and the people who surrounded us. If you grew up with a parent who constantly commented on your weight or criticised the food choices you made, you may have formed the belief that being 'fat' isn't acceptable. By extension, you might have grown up believing you need to be thin to be loved. That belief system then shaped your relationship with food and your body well into adulthood. And so on. And it isn't your fault.

I carried my negative belief system with me throughout my teens and was only able to uncover it when I went to a therapist. I realised my belief system was why I was obsessed with being thin. Thankfully, I had access to the tools and knowledge I needed to turn this mindset around, and my life has changed beyond recognition since then.

# Creating this handbook

Today, I live the healthy life and I've built my brand, JSHealth, around the principles that have helped me feel the best I've ever felt. I'm passionate about helping women to free themselves from the vicious cycle of dieting, calorie counting, daily weigh-ins and obsessing about how much they eat. This kind of life is a self-made prison, full of unhappiness and negative self-talk – I know this because I spent many years living in that prison myself.

In my two previous books, *The Healthy Life* and *Living the Healthy Life*, I shared my journey to health and healing, and led you down the path

I took to get to a place of peace. This book is a culmination of everything I've learned. For years now, I've been completely immersed in the health and wellness world. I've spent countless hours researching, creating (and testing) recipes, and consulting with clients and my community on a huge range of health issues. I've been asked excellent questions, and I've pooled my resources to answer them.

And, based on all of that work, I've pulled out 12 principles that have created profound change – in both my life, and the lives of those in my incredible, inspiring JSHealth community.

This is a handbook you can hold on to, forever. The most valuable knowledge I have is on these pages. I want you to refer to this book whenever you have a question, or whenever you need a little reassurance that you're not alone.

And here's the most amazing news: this healthy life doesn't involve dieting, cutting out food groups, counting calories, starving yourself or slogging away at the gym to exhaustion. It's about balance, and speaking to yourself with kindness and understanding. It's about recognising old patterns, and moving away from them towards a calmer existence.

The 12 principles in this book will help you to clear the confusion, give up fad dieting and, at last, find balance with food and make peace with your body. These principles complement and support each other, making it easier to achieve that balance we all crave.

Making the changes in this book doesn't have to be hard, but, like any major shift in life, it all starts in the mind. If you've dieted before, you'll know how easy it is to feel so overwhelmed that you just want to give up, and put the healthy life in the 'too-hard basket'. This isn't your fault – I see it all the time. But trust me, this will change after reading this book. The healthy life will no longer feeling confusing or overwhelming.

While you work through the 12 principles in this book, you might discover that certain habits or mindsets are holding you back from achieving your health (and happiness) goals. If you can become aware of those things, and then kindly and gently detach from them, you'll be able to tear down the negative belief systems that have taken hold after years of following trendy diets and all-or-nothing workout regimes or scrolling through Insta feeds full of 'perfect' bodies.

As you begin to flick through these pages, all I ask of you is that you be kinder to yourself. Please release any pressure you may be feeling to read this book and do every single thing in it – and do it all perfectly.

I believe in slow and steady change.

## The healthy way, for life

JSHealth was born from my deep desire to help women understand that they can still live a healthy life and feel good about their bodies without being on a diet or punishing themselves. Women are ready for a new way. Women are ready for balance. Women are ready to treat their bodies with kindness, not punishment.

Fad diets are out. Balance is in. My balanced eating philosophy has helped women reach their health goals without dieting and without deprivation. (Yes, really!) This type of eating leads to long-term success, and it's a lifestyle you can maintain and ENJOY for life.

This philosophy is the result of my own personal journey, as well as my nutritional studies and the time I've spent with patients in my nutrition practice. It happened quite organically.

The truth is, I was raised in a healthy household. My family has been health-conscious since day one, and my mum is the best healthy cook in the world. She's my biggest inspiration! Sadly, I lost sight of this strong foundation during my teenage and early adult years, but I made my way back to it after struggling for so long.

If I had to describe my approach to eating in a word, it'd be **flexible**. I believe in eating well MOST of the time, and leaving room for indulgence. This way, you can still eat out, sip wine and sample that delicious dessert. Cheers to that!

My thoughts about food are consistent and haven't changed since my first two books. I've received hundreds of messages from people saying they're absolutely thriving since they started following my health principles. There's nothing that makes me happier!

But since eating is something we do three or more times a day (hopefully), I'm going to take you through my food philosophy in Chapter 3. If you're already on the healthy-eating bandwagon, that's great! A bit of positive reinforcement won't hurt and, who knows, you might pick up something that you didn't last time.

If you're new to this whole eating-for-fuel thing, then sit back, relax and read carefully – you're taking an amazing step towards lifelong health, and I'm so proud of you.

# Why diets don't work

Before we delve into the practices that do work in the long term, it's important that we talk about what doesn't work. Diets are at the top of this list. In fact, diets make it much harder to achieve a healthy mind and body.

It's true that some diets work in the short term; some of them – like intermittent fasting – may even be supported by solid research and good health benefits. On certain diets you may lose weight and see good results. But I've yet to meet anyone who's been able to stick to a diet for longer than 3–6 months! True story.

The simple truth is that diets don't work in the long run; they're not sustainable. They're not designed to be realistic to our lifestyle. After a while, you just can't do it anymore. You crack and end up undoing all of your hard work. And, what's worse, doing this can really mess up your metabolism and negatively effect your relationship with food, long term.

Think about it: you start a diet. You restrict your food intake. You may lose weight. But after a short time, you can't handle the deprivation anymore, so your body rebels. You may overeat or binge. Your body stops you from going back into starvation mode by holding on to fat. So you

gain back the weight you lost, and maybe even a little more. Then you decide to go on a diet again – usually on a Monday! And the vicious cycle starts again.

The research backs this up too. A study of long-term dieters found that years of restricting calories reduced their metabolic rates by 13 per cent. That is major. Another study confirmed this, reporting that low-calorie dieting slowed down metabolism.

From my own clinical experience, I can tell you that people who get caught up in this toxic cycle (I was one of them) find it harder to maintain a healthy, consistent weight.

Professor of psychology Traci Mann has conducted studies on the relationship between restrictive dieting and successful weight loss. Mann notes that 'weight regain is the typical long-term response to dieting, rather than the exception.' She goes on to say that 'calorie deprivation leads to changes in hormones, metabolism and cognitive/attentional functions that make it difficult to enact the behaviours needed to keep weight off.'

In plain English? Calorie counting and restriction lead to an obsession with food – and that obsession overrides any willpower to stick to the diet. Dieters almost always regain their lost weight within a few years.

*Dieting* = deprivation + restriction

deprivation + restriction = obsession + *anxiety* **around food**

which = guilty feelings + *self loathing*

which = bingeing + *overeating*

Diets strain our relationship with food and our bodies, causing us to focus on weight, not health. They encourage us to count calories, restrict our food intake and control our cravings, which can often lead to disordered eating or even just an emotionally complex relationship with food. Diets also tend to instil 'fear' around certain food groups, and that isn't healthy.

One study surveyed twenty dieters who said they were unable to maintain diets because they were unrealistic, unsustainable, boring or too expensive. One dieter said, 'it made me think constantly about my next meal.' Others said diets didn't address their lifestyles, and focused on food rather than changing their behaviour. Some said they were 'confused about which choices were correct, because of the different messages they were given by different diet companies'.

# My thoughts on fasting

In my clinic, I've also noticed that those on the 5:2 diet (and similar diets) tend to obsess about food. It consumes them. By now you know that I don't think this is healthy. It doesn't support a healthy relationship with food in the long term.

If fasting works for you, that's great! I'm not here to judge or criticise that. Eat in a way that works for you and your body – no one else's.

But diets are gruelling – and unnecessary. They require a huge amount of dedication, focus, energy and control. Not only is this very stressful, it also isn't natural. The best diet for your weight is a balanced, wholefood diet eaten with mindfulness and moderation. It's realistic and manageable. It will help you to feel full and satiated after every meal, and reduce your cravings, overeating and emotional eating.

My philosophy is about giving up dieting for good, and finding a more balanced approach to food. It's time to give up quick fixes and fads. This is about adopting a sustainable lifestyle that you can ENJOY.

I have spent the last five years connecting to the beautiful JSHealth community through social media and my program. I have watched the members of this community turn away from fad dieting and extremes and find freedom with food and their bodies. They've reconnected with their bodies' needs, and they eat with flexibility. By following these principles, which promote balance, these people have been able to reach their goals for health and happiness. Nothing – nothing – makes me prouder.

# Diets and disordered eating

Fearing food can cause you to feel anxious and stressed around mealtimes. This, in turn, can lead to a degree of disordered eating or even orthorexia (an unhealthy obsession with the healthy life). This mentality can be hard to shake off, and it's my biggest concern for young girls of this generation.

Fad diets encourage us to fear foods, and that's not healthy for the mind or body. I always say that an obsession with 'clean' or 'healthy' eating is NOT healthy at all.

If you follow my work, you'll know that I'm deeply passionate about helping women to overcome disordered eating patterns and build a positive body image. I believe this is more important that eating your greens and exercising every day – I truly do.

Your relationship with your body is the foundation for the healthy life. When you love your body, you treat it with care and kindness. You don't punish it. With self-love, balance happens naturally.

**Isn't it about time we felt *good* about *food* and our bodies?**

# How to use this book

You can go through each of my 12 essential steps one at a time or you can choose the individual steps that speak to you. Each step will help you find freedom with food, reset your mind and body and achieve long-lasting results. This isn't like my regular recipe books, but you will find 50 of my best recipes to assist you on your journey. Remember to use the key on the opposite page to navigate dietary requirements and the macronutrients.

**1**    Commit to tactics and tips to reset your mind in Chapters 1, 2, 5, 10 and 12.

**2**    Set up strategies to reset your food in Chapters 3, 4, 6, 8, 9 and 11.

**3**    Manage your stress and reset your body in Chapters 4, 7 and 8.

**4**    Find 50 of my best recipes:

Build a meal   *48, 66*
Breakfast   *68, 102*
Food prep   *102*
One-pan dinners   *154*
Snacks   *176, 184*
Desserts   *217*

*See opposite page*

Reset your mind

Reset your food

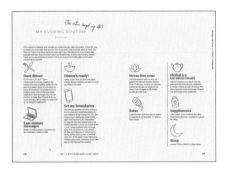

Manage your stress and reset your body

## Key

**GF**
gluten-free

**DF**
dairy-free

**VEG**
vegetarian

**VEGAN**

**PROTEIN**

**FIBRE**

**CARBS**

**GOOD FAT**

Build a meal

Breakfast

Food prep

One-pan dinners

Snacks

Desserts

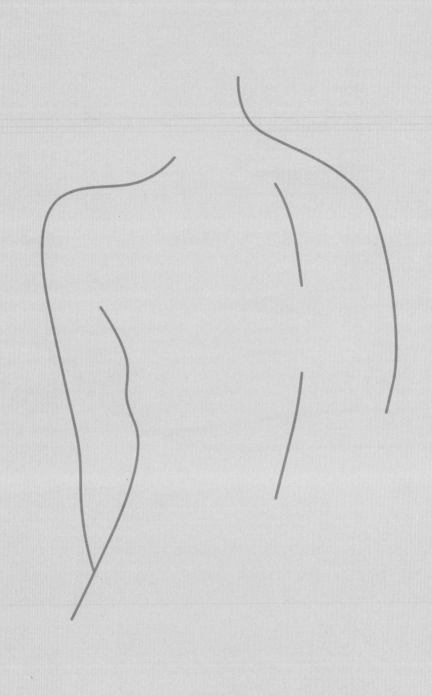

# 1

# Give up the numbers game

---

*I threw out my scales and stopped counting calories, and I've never felt better.*

# Chasing skinny

Between the ages of thirteen and twenty-four, the scales ruled my life, and I don't say that lightly. They were my safety blanket, and a mirror for my self-worth. I'd step onto them every morning, and the number I saw would determine my mood, and how good I felt about myself for the rest of the day. It would also dictate my eating choices: if the number was higher than the previous day, I'd restrict my eating to get back on track. But after an exhausting day of self-inflicted punishment, my cravings would inevitably kick in, and I'd end up bingeing on all the foods I'd been depriving myself of. On the other hand, if I liked the number that popped up, I'd try to squeeze in an extra workout so I could subtract another 200 calories from my daily total to be even 'better'. Chasing skinny felt good.

It breaks my heart to write that, but it did. This 'control' gave me a false sense of confidence; it made me feel like I was accomplishing my goals, but looking back, I see that the scales always led to a lose–lose situation. Being a slave to them actually made it harder for me to maintain a healthy, consistent weight. I certainly didn't feel good about myself, and I was completely disconnected from my body. This was my sad, toxic reality for more than a decade.

My inability to follow a fad diet 'perfectly' and reach my 'perfect' weight caused me to hate and punish myself. And this hatred didn't stop at my daily weigh-in. After hopping off the scales, I'd head for an intense workout, and then eat a low-calorie breakfast such as a black coffee with lots of artificial sweetener, and diet yoghurt with diet jelly. I'd measure every morsel of food, and if I went over my calorie allowance, I saw it as a failure. I was always tired and hungry, and the pressure of dieting and exercising stripped me of energy.

The craziest thing about all of this was that I thought I was healthy! In hindsight, I see that I was weight-obsessed and focusing far too much on the physical stuff, rather than on my inner health – which is where the magic happens.

- Do you relate?
- Are you weighing yourself each morning?
- Are you allowing that number to affect your eating habits for the rest of the day?
- Are you seeing that number as a reflection of who you are?
- Are you giving the scales too much power?
- Are you aspiring to be at a weight from when you were much younger?

It's time to stop this madness.
I've said it countless times before, and I'll say it again:

> The *number* on the scales does NOT determine your self-worth.

# I threw out the scales to find peace with my body

I will never forget the day I threw out my scales; it was the most incredible, liberating feeling, and it was also the day I found freedom with food.

Let me set the scene for you ...

I was twenty-four years old. I'd just weighed myself at home, like I did every morning, and I didn't like the results. I'd been doing everything 'right', so why wasn't I seeing that 'perfect' number I had in my mind? I couldn't believe it, so I picked up the scales and moved around the house with them, hoping the different floorboards would somehow change the number. (Scary, but true.) I hopped on and off and turned my body every which way to get that magic number to appear. I was actually cradling the scales, which I'd owned for over ten years, in my arms as I walked around the house.

Obviously, my plan didn't work.

I fell to the floor and burst into tears. I was in no way overweight, but I hadn't achieved my idea of the 'perfect' weight, and I was so angry with myself. Luckily, my boyfriend (now my husband), Dean, was home. He saw me holding the scales and having an emotional breakdown. I was completely, utterly vulnerable. He sat down next to me and gently said, 'Jess, you cannot do this to yourself anymore.'

Deep down, I knew he was right. I knew I had to make a change otherwise I'd never be able to repair my relationship with my body.

He continued, 'Jess, we are throwing out these scales.'

I was PETRIFIED, and I mean that. I was addicted to monitoring my weight. So many thoughts ran through my head: What? No! I can't. I've had these scales forever. How will I measure my health – my self-worth – without them? How will I start my day without knowing how much I weigh? How?

But, at the same time, I also felt a sense of relief and freedom at Dean's suggestion. I let myself imagine what my days could be like minus the torment, scrutiny and pressure of hitting those 'perfect' numbers.

Together, we walked down the street and tossed the scales into a skip. Believe me, I tried to talk myself (and Dean) out of it along the way, but he wouldn't budge. I couldn't believe I was actually doing it. And then I did it! With that, I let go of my habit of daily self-inflicted punishment and welcomed a whole lot of self-love into my life.

The relief was real. It was immediate and tangible. I felt so free.

I haven't weighed myself since that day.

Throwing out the scales gave me the space I needed to heal.

Fast-forward to today and I still don't know what I weigh. I'm not obsessed with my weight. I live the healthy life and I connect to how I feel in my body, and guess what? I fit comfortably in my clothes and I know that my weight has balanced out to a point that it's easy to maintain.

Eating a meal has become a joy instead of a challenge. I feel so light in my body and mind and I'm enjoying every moment.

You deserve the same freedom.

# Why throwing out the scales will set you free

If you're currently trapped in the cycle of weighing yourself daily, like I was, the number on the scales has the power to cause immense stress, and trigger emotional eating and even weight yo-yoing. When I used to weigh myself, all sorts of anxious questions would run through my head: What will the number be? Will it be higher or lower than yesterday? Has my 'hard work' paid off?

Here are a few ways throwing out your scales can help you on your health journey.

## You'll lower your cortisol levels

My personal opinion is that the daily weigh-in is adding stress to your mind and body. Stress increases our levels of cortisol (the stress hormone), which can lead us to gain weight around our mid-section. Cortisol can also decrease thyroid function – the thyroid gland is the driver of our metabolism. When combined with the stress caused by the constant restriction and deprivation of dieting, the spike in cortisol that comes with weighing yourself daily can make weight balance very hard to achieve. Plus, starting your day with a weigh-in adds pressure to your life, and that's not healthy for your mind or body. Pressure negatively affects our relationship with food – we'll explore this more in Chapter 7.

*I always say,* **Heavy thoughts = heavy body.**

**Light thoughts = light body.**

## You'll learn to love the body you have,

## not the body you *had*

Our bodies change as we age in so many ways, so we can't expect to weigh the same at thirty as we did when we were a teenager or a young adult. We have to let go of that number and stop trying to squeeze back into our high-school jeans. Instead, the focus should be on feeling energetic and happy in our own skin, no matter what stage of life we're in.

'Please, let go of that "perfect" number in your mind.'

## You'll enjoy a healthier relationship
## with your body

Weighing yourself prevents you from building a healthy relationship with your body. When you ride the roller-coaster of numbers, any disappointment you feel can steer you away from your healthy journey. You might punish yourself by restricting food and/or doing too much high-intensity exercise. This extreme approach always backfires in the long run.

# Stop counting calories

Around the same time I threw out the scales, I managed to kick another one of my addictions: I stopped counting carbs and calories.

Calorie and carb counting was my addiction, and one that made me afraid of food. I was so good at it that you could ask me right now about the calorie content of any food, and I'd be able to tell you. Those numbers are stuck in my head, and they haunt me.

Sadly, all that adding and subtracting led me to see food in an unhealthy and obsessive way. (How could it not?) It also added an enormous amount of stress and pressure to my everyday life, which didn't help me to control my weight in the long term.

Calorie counting is a game. You're told to restrict your food intake to reach a certain number, and if you hit it, you feel like you're achieving something, so you keep going for a period of time. The key word here is 'period'. Usually, after a SHORT time, your mind and body rebel. You break the diet or go over your designated calorie intake, and that turns on the tap of self-criticism. You hate yourself for failing to stick to the number so you go back to calorie counting – only this time you reduce the amount of calories you're going to eat in order to make up for your dietary 'sins'. Eventually, those feelings of failure will bubble up to the surface, and you succumb to overeating and bingeing on all those forbidden foods.

But here's the thing, it's not your fault.

As we've already discussed, diets are not realistic!

That's why, when I walked down the street to toss out my treasured set of scales, I also made a commitment to give up calorie counting and dieting. I decided to let go of the 'My diet starts on Monday' mentality, and this added to my HUGE sense of freedom and relief.

When you relieve the pressure and choose balance, you can start to heal your relationship with food and your body. And this healing happens so naturally and effortlessly. Who wants to be counting numbers every meal for the rest of their lives?! Counting numbers at every meal makes it really hard to connect to your hunger signals, which can lead to overeating.

# It's time to take action

Are you ready to free yourself from the obsession with numbers? These three steps will help you do exactly that.

1   Please, go into your bathroom right now and throw out the scales. If you're not up for that just yet, give them to a family member to hide for at least 3 months.

2   Next, throw out your old skinny jeans and delete any calorie-counting apps from your phone. Unfollow people on social media who promote crazy diets or unrealistic 'bikini bodies'. And please, stop googling diets and detoxes too.

3   Forget the idea of 'perfect eating' and calorie counting and commit to lifelong balance instead. No more shortcuts, no extremes, no quick fixes; they don't work. If they did, would you be reading this book?

If you can do each of these things, you'll find you have the space to relax and repair your relationship with your body. And then you can follow the rest of the steps in this book to create a lifestyle you will be able to maintain, now and forever.

## But, Jess, what if I still want to lose weight?

Don't worry. You can STILL achieve weight loss by giving up the scales and fad diets. In fact, scientists have found that between one- to two-thirds of dieters actually regain more weight than they initially lost. This cycle of losing weight, gaining it, then dieting to lose it again, is known as weight cycling.

By shifting to a more balanced approach to food and exercise – one that steers away from extremes – your body will be better equipped not only to lose weight, but also to keep it off in the long term.

I want you to know that there is another way to achieve your health goals – a kinder, more consistent and realistic way. When you make the decision to give up diets and extremes, and live a healthy life, your weight will naturally balance out. I wrote this book to help you get there.

**You can achieve your** *best weight* **without** *obsessing* **over numbers.**

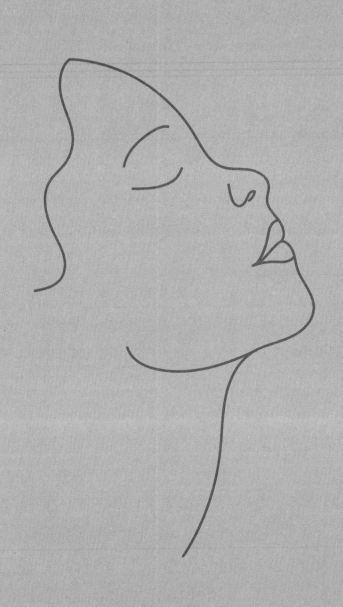

# Speak to yourself with kindness

---

*Like anyone, I have negative thoughts about myself and my body. But when I have these thoughts, I remind myself to be kind and gentle.*

# Your mindset is everything

You might be surprised to hear this, but I believe that kindness is the most transformational tool you can take away from this book. And here's why: after years of personal healing, studying health and practising nutrition, the most life-changing lesson I've learned is this:

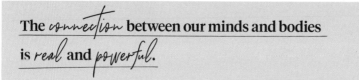

The *connection* between our minds and bodies is *real* and *powerful.*

The state of our mental and emotional health affects our physical body in so many ways. If you're trying to heal your relationship with food and your body, the first – and most important – thing you need to tackle is changing your mindset. If you're trying to reach your health goals and foster a more wholesome relationship with your body, you have to address your current belief system and start speaking to yourself with kindness and respect, and with less judgement. It's not easy to change the way you think, but you'll get better at it with practice. And, while you're doing that, you'll notice your body changing too.

The power of the mind is profound. Here's what I've learned from my own journey:

- How you talk to yourself matters.
- Your thoughts impact your body both physically and emotionally.
- Your thoughts affect how much abundance you attract to your everyday life.
- Your belief systems dictate how you live your life.
- Your body listens to your thoughts. Be kind.

Your *mindset* matters most when it comes to living the healthy life. A positive mindset will *set you free.*

A positive mindset will enable you to sustain your healthy habits and maintain the results in the long term. And this is another reason why diets don't work: diets don't teach us how to develop healthier thoughts towards our body and ourselves. All they do is bully us into abiding by rules, and restricting and depriving ourselves of certain foods.

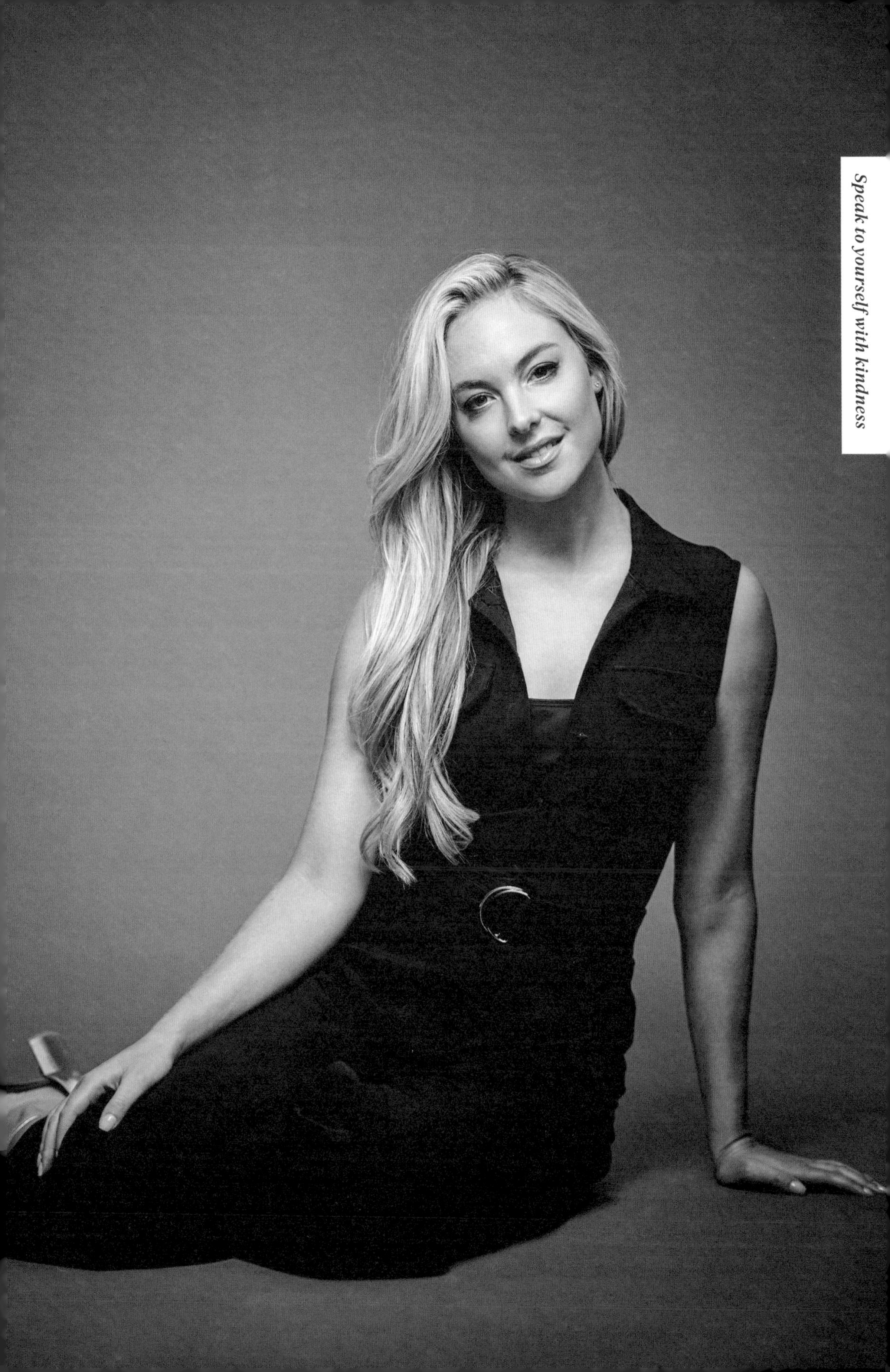

Often, diets make us see ourselves in a negative light. We're more judgemental and critical of our bodies and our food choices. This was certainly the case for me. I believe dieting caused my body-image issues and negative self-talk. And that constant chatter made it incredibly hard for me to feel like I was 'enough'. They also didn't give me the space I needed to connect to my body, as I was too busy being connected to the diet rules.

> ✳ Change your mindset, and you'll start to *see results*
>
> ✳ Change your mindset, and *healthy choices* will be easier to make.
>
> ✳ Change your mindset, and you'll be able to maintain your healthy habits *for life.*

All of the strategies in this chapter will help you to change any beliefs that aren't serving you on your journey to health and happiness.

- By speaking to yourself with kindness, you'll learn that you deserve to love and be loved.
- By being self-aware, you'll create a new story for yourself.
- By knowing you are worthy of a good life, you'll reduce your suffering.
- By ditching dieting and extremes, you'll realise that perfection doesn't exist.
- By forgiving yourself, you'll let go of the past and live in the present.

# I spent years stuck in a negative mindset

During my teens and early twenties, I struggled with toxic thoughts towards my body. I felt heavy, tired and low every day. As a result, I battled body dysmorphia and had an incredibly negative body image. I also had anxiety – especially around food.

I often woke up feeling depressed and anxious, and I would doubt myself all day long. I'll never forget the days when my worries were so intense I'd get a physical ache in the centre of my stomach. The way I was speaking to myself had a ripple effect on every area of my life.

When I woke up, I spoke negatively to myself. 'Jess, you're not doing enough. You look fat. You don't even know what you want to do with your life. You have no purpose.'

When I ate, I spoke negatively to myself. 'You should have eaten less. You should have chosen better food. You shouldn't have ordered dessert.'

When I exercised, I spoke negatively to myself. 'You're not training hard or often enough. Your hips look big. Your stomach is so bloated.'

I felt so alone in my thoughts, even though I had the most wonderful family and group of friends. Despite having so many blessings in my life, I believed the world was against me. I had a typical victim mentality and would always think, 'Why do bad things always happen to me?' or 'When will it be my turn?'

An entire day of not feeling 'enough' would hit me like a ton of bricks at night. I'd berate myself with: 'You just can't get it right, can you, Jess?'; 'The diet must start tomorrow.'; 'You need to do more.'; 'You need to be thinner/prettier/smarter to be accepted.' Hello, insomnia! Now I believe the universe is on my side, but back then I felt like a failure at life. Maybe that sounds dramatic, but it was truly how I felt. Does any of this sound familiar?

# When I changed my mindset, life became wonderful

Soon after I shifted to a more positive line of thought, my physical body started to change too. My anxiety dissipated. I felt lighter, freer and more in control of my thoughts. With my newfound positive mindset, I got out of the dieting trap and began healing my relationship with food. I cared about myself too much to put my body through another torturous diet.

This new positive mindset attracted abundance and peace into my life; instead of feeling that my life was lacking, I felt that health and happiness were within my reach.

My relationships with my family, friends and work colleagues have become incredibly peaceful. There's no drama or conflict. I know so many people wish they had more peace in their lives. If you're one of them, please know that you deserve that.

## Am I 100 per cent healed?

No way! This is a journey. I heal more and more each day, and I don't put pressure on myself to be perfect. I'm much less judgemental and self-critical these days, and I'm also better at forgiving myself.

In all honesty, I'd say my relationship with food is 95 per cent healed. For me, that's incredible. I can't recall the last time I binged or felt anxiety, guilt or fear around mealtimes. Travel is the only thing that triggers those thoughts, but thankfully I now have the tools I need to take care of myself in those moments. I still struggle with negative body image sometimes, and I'll share my strategies for dealing with that in Chapter 10.

This shift in mindset didn't happen overnight, though. And it wasn't easy to train my mind to think differently. But it was well worth the work, because it's had an unbelievable effect on my health, and my life overall.

It will do the same for you. Let's dig in!

# How to shift your mindset

These are the tactics and tips I used to turn my negative mindset into a positive and abundant one. If you can commit to thinking healthier, kinder thoughts, you'll feel so much lighter and better about yourself and your life. I'm excited for you to feel that freedom.

## 1  Stop fighting your thoughts

I actually learned this concept through yoga and it has changed my life. Here's how it works: instead of attaching to your thoughts and believing every thought, just be a witness to them. Don't judge them or fight them; simply be aware of them and lean into them.

When we struggle with negative thoughts, our natural instinct is to fight against them. But that actually encourages those thoughts to keep flooding in. On the other hand, if you accept them, you'll notice they start to fade faster and more permanently. Quite amazing.

(Read that again if you need to.)

For example, when I'm in a yoga pose that feels uncomfortable, my mind tries to take over. It says, 'You can't do this.' I used to judge myself if I couldn't go into a pose perfectly. But now I accept that I've done my best, and I don't give in to the negativity or attach myself to those thoughts. Since changing my mindset, my yoga practice has improved tenfold. I enjoy it so much more.

The same principle applies to everyday life.

## 2  Don't believe every thought

Don't attach to every thought, simply be witness to them. Our thoughts are not always true. Sometimes, our ego influences the story we tell ourselves. Sometimes, our environment affects the way we think. We may find ourselves saying things like, 'I'm not smart enough to apply for that job,' or 'People don't like being around me because I'm boring,' or 'I don't deserve a pay rise because my work isn't good enough.'

We make up these stories in our minds, accept them as the truth and then we attach to them. And not all of our thoughts have meaning, they're just thoughts.

In these cases, our ego takes over to challenge our deep fears and knock down self-esteem.

Spiritual author Eckhart Tolle explains this well. He says, 'Ego is much more than an overinflated sense of self. It can also turn up in feelings of inferiority or self-hatred because ego is any image you have of yourself that gives you a sense of identity – and that identity derives from the things you tell yourself and the things other people have been saying about you that you've decided to accept as truth.'

THE 12-STEP MIND-BODY-FOOD RESET

When negative thoughts pop up often enough, we believe them and allow them to become part of our identity, but they don't define us. Sometimes, they're not even true. Don't give in to every thought.

Awareness is everything. If you can be conscious of your thought patterns, you'll create space to heal. If you know your triggers, you'll be able to process the thoughts when they pop up and bat them away. And, as a result, you'll develop a kinder relationship with yourself and your body.

'When we struggle with negative thoughts, our natural instinct is to fight against them. But that actually encourages those thoughts to keep flooding in.'

## 3 Speak kindly to yourself

After observing my thoughts, I speak to myself kindly. When we're struggling with negative thoughts, we tend to beat ourselves up over it. Through years of yoga practice, therapy and self-healing, I've found that speaking to myself with kindness and less judgement actually reduces the negative conversation in my mind.

So the next time you're dealing with negative thoughts, try having a kind and gentle conversation with yourself – like you would with your bestie. Think about where the thoughts may be coming from. Don't push them away. Listen to them, without judgement, and accept them.

When you choose to be kind to yourself, it doesn't leave much room for negativity.

## 4 Stop with the comparisons

Comparison can often be traced to a lack of self-worth, and it's so toxic. For many years, I compared myself to everyone else, and social media didn't help – it only encourages everyone to pretend they're living the high life 24/7. This was the main reason I set up social media boundaries (see Chapter 5 for more). My negative mindset had a trickle-down effect on my wellbeing. My thoughts drained any energy I had to live my best life. Instead, I attracted negative people, situations and relationships. It was exhausting!

But thankfully, I realised that comparing myself to others was making me feel stuck. It wasn't driving my life forward in any way – far from it. Comparison actually pushes us ten steps back. Now, when I catch myself comparing, I try to understand why I'm not feeling good enough in that moment. I question what this person or situation has triggered within me, and I ease myself out of that thought by thinking about something I'm proud of or grateful for – like my family, friends, health or work.

Keeping my head and heart focused on my goals is important to me, so I do everything in my power to stop comparison in its tracks and put my energy towards achieving my dreams. Because there's enough good stuff in life for everyone! And just because someone has something you don't, or is doing something amazing, doesn't mean you can't also have that thing or do something great too. So let's quit comparing and start thinking more abundantly from now on. We can all create success. We can all find love, health and happiness. We all deserve it.

## 5    Replace negative thoughts with positive ones

It's time to view your life through a positive lens, and that starts with swapping one thought at a time. Here's a powerful exercise for you to try. Over time, you'll start to do it automatically in your head. Whenever you have a negative thought about yourself, you'll gently replace it with a positive one without even needing to write it down.

Fake it till you make it if necessary! Then, as your mindset shifts, those positive thoughts will become more authentic.

*Activity

# FIND THE
# POSITIVE THOUGHT

**1**    On a piece of paper, write down all the negative things you say to yourself. When you look in the mirror, what do you think? For example, 'I shouldn't have eaten that.' 'I should be skinnier.' 'I feel fat and bloated.' 'I have no self-control around food.' 'I wish my legs were more toned.'

**2**    Choose the three most common negative thoughts that keep popping up.

**3**    Now replace each negative thought with a positive thought. For example, 'I'm so grateful my legs can walk and carry me through my day.' 'I choose to focus on being healthy and happy, not skinny.' 'My body can digest food well.' Write these new positive thoughts on a new piece of paper.

**4**    Stick these three positive thoughts on your bathroom mirror or bedroom wall and look at them each day. Subconsciously, they'll help to change your conscious thought patterns.

       THE 12-STEP MIND-BODY-FOOD RESET

## Set boundaries with social media

Social media was designed as a way for us to share our stories and experiences with others, but unfortunately, it's become a space of comparison. It can trigger self-doubt, lower our self-esteem, increase body anxiety and intensify negative self-talk. As much as people talk about 'keeping it real' on social media, nine times out of ten we only see the good. People tend not to post about the struggles they deal with day to day; we see only the highlights. And we don't see realistic bodies; we scroll through 'bikini bodies' that are Photoshopped to the max.

But social media has become a part of life. Most of us are on it, and we check our feeds multiple times a day (let's be honest). There are tons of people who use it in a positive way. I'm an active social media user, and I love the way it helps me to connect and engage with my community. But I'm aware that it affects me, so I limit my use. See page 82 for some of my favourite ways to scale back on social media.

## View your heath as a lifestyle, not a fad

When it comes to health, so many of us latch on to extremes. We do juice fasts and skinny-tea detoxes; sign up for restrictive diets and hard-core fitness programs; and push our bodies to the limit. And then we beat ourselves up when the results don't last. The truth is, health isn't a fad. Deep down, I know you know this.

Those quick fixes and extremes don't work. They're not sustainable. We need to think long term. Health is a forever commitment, and it's the best investment you'll ever make. The next time you feel tempted by a fad, remind yourself how short-lived the results are.

Once you start to look at health and wellness as a lifestyle and something you can maintain forever, everything will fall into place.

You'll find that healthy choices become more natural and consistent. This is because the principles associated with the healthy life that I've outlined in this book are realistic, manageable and enjoyable – and therefore easy to practise for years rather than weeks.

You'll want to continue this life, and that's pretty amazing!

## Forgive yourself for your past

Please stop punishing yourself for whatever happened in the past. If you're angry with yourself, forgive and let go. You did the best you could with what you knew at the time. We're human, and we learn as we live. We all make mistakes. We all have moments in our lives when we're just not the best versions of ourselves. Hard times often make us stronger and wiser.

If you're currently in a challenging time in your life, please know it can and will get better. Try to see a therapist to deal with the pain and understand where it may be coming from. You don't have to go through this alone. Also, know you are not the only one experiencing these feelings. Everyone is struggling in some way, but not everyone speaks about it. Sometimes it helps to write a letter of forgiveness to yourself. Whenever I do this, I feel a huge sense of relief.

For example, my letter might say:

> *Dear Jess,*
>
> *Please forgive me for speaking/acting the way I did. I didn't mean it. I was doing the best I could with what I knew. I was in pain and trying to manage it. I love you. Forgive me. I am ready to heal.*

## Go from hateful to grateful

Our belief system influences how we view ourselves, and the world. It guides our everyday lives and it's a powerful thing. When your belief system shifts, you'll stop seeing things from a victim's viewpoint and will start to feel grateful for all that you already have. Focusing on what you're grateful for will set you up to feel worthy when more good things come into your life.

**Victim mentality:** If you wake up feeling like the universe is against you, you'll carry this mentality with you throughout the day, and it will cause you to see just about every situation in a negative light. With a victim mentality, you may think thoughts like: 'This always happens to me!' 'I can never get it right.' 'When will it be my turn?'

**Feeling unworthy:** When you have a negative mindset, you may feel unworthy of better things and situations. You may have thoughts like these: 'I don't deserve that promotion.' or 'I'm not going to be able to have a better life.'

**Grateful mentality:** On the other hand, if you feel supported by people/ the world, grateful for all that you already have, and worthy of having it, you'll feel more positive about the future and you'll attract more love, success and abundance into your life.

We have to start believing that the universe is on our side. Gabrielle Bernstein talks about this mindset shift in her book, *The Universe Has Your Back*. Reading this book was a huge help for me, and I highly recommend it if you feel stuck in a victim mindset.

# 10 Relieve the pressure

As you work on healing your relationship with your body, and tune in to what's affecting your mindset and eating patterns, you'll start identifying the added sources of your stress. You'll also realise just how much pressure you're feeling.

Pressure can trigger anxiety, negative body image, emotional eating and dieting. Women are especially great at putting pressure on themselves to do it all – to be perfect mums, partners, sisters, friends and career women, all while eating perfectly and maintaining a perfect weight. This pressure is innate for so many of us.

To heal your relationship with food and your body, you need to relieve this pressure. Start by acknowledging the sources of your stress, and by accepting that you're not expected to do it all, or do it all perfectly.

Remind yourself of this daily. Then work through these steps:

1 **Know that you're doing your best.** People in our lives often have unrealistic expectations of us, and it's okay to disappoint them sometimes. It's just a part of living. You have to make peace with the idea of not being able to please everyone all the time.

2 **Give yourself more praise.** You have to start to acknowledge all the things you DO every day. When you put yourself down, think of a few things you've done today or this week that you're proud of. These can be as simple as saying no to someone's request when you needed to rest. It could be something as satisfying as finishing a great work project.

3 **Dig deep to uncover where these expectations are coming from.** Perhaps your parents instilled this pressure in you? Perhaps you're an A-type personality who can't help but feel pressure to do more work? A therapist can support you as you figure out the sources of your pressure and ways to release it.

4 **Don't take things too personally.**

## TESTIMONIAL

*'My goal was to love my body regardless of the outcome, and I ended up losing 14 kilos in six months!'*

## 11 Let go of the guilt around food

I believe that feeling guilty about food prevents healing. Guilt manifests as heaviness and stress in the body, and I believe that when we fill our minds with these 'heavy' thoughts, they weigh us down; when we look in the mirror, we see a heavier version of ourselves.

To have a healthy relationship with food, you have to allow yourself a little freedom and leeway.

Some days, you'll eat super well and exercise, and other days you'll indulge a little and find you're too lazy to exercise. This is balance, and balance is healthy.

A night out with your girlfriends and a couple of glasses of wine is good for the soul – why punish yourself the next morning?

A scoop of gelato on a hot summer's day is a delicious treat – why kick yourself for enjoying your life?

If you feel you've overindulged, just remember that tomorrow is a new day, and you can make better choices. It's all going to be okay. Trade in a guilty thought for a positive action. For example: 'Today, I didn't feel great after eating so much sugar. Tomorrow, I'll eat less of it.'

Eating is something you'll be doing every day for the rest of your life. It's essential for survival, but a lot of us give food too much power. If you've made unhealthy choices, don't stress or beat yourself up, as this often leads to bingeing. Take back control.

The guilty feelings will pass. I promise.

Be kind to yourself. Let. It. Go.

### What to do if you're feeling guilty about food

Close your eyes, take a big, deep breath, and then let it go slowly.

If that doesn't work, try writing down what you're feeling anxious or guilty about. Transferring the thoughts from your head onto paper can help to get them out of your head.

Or practise yoga or meditation. Go to a class or simply work your way through a few poses in the privacy of your home. This simple act will help you to reconnect with your body and calm your thoughts.

## 12 Lean in to vulnerability

It's okay to have hard, sad or painful times.

This is part of life.

Usually the hard times are our biggest learning experience. Life is full of really good times and really hard times. We need both to live our best life.

# 13 Believe in the Law of Attraction

The Law of Attraction states that you'll attract whatever you focus on into your life. So if you're giving something energy and attention, you increase the chances of it becoming a reality. I believe in this law wholeheartedly as well as the power of visualisation and manifestation, and it's brought so much abundance to my life. You CAN live the life you've always wanted. You just have to dream it and believe you're worthy of it.

When I started shifting my mentality from negative to positive, my worldview changed with it. I believed that I could do and achieve anything I put my mind to. Slowly, but surely, I'm turning my dreams into reality.

The beauty of manifesting is that it's all on you. You can choose what you want. You can decide your dreams. Here are three of my favourite ways to harness the power of manifestation.

1  **Say positive affirmations daily.** Positive affirmations work best when they're in the present tense. For example, say: 'I'm healthy. I'm thankful for my body. I attract health and abundance.' This will put you in a positive frame of mind. If you tell yourself you're going to have a good day, you probably will!

2  **Do a manifestation practice.** Visualise what you want, and then put that out into the universe. For example, you could take this opportunity to visualise your dream job or home. Wake up to this vision every day and feel the happiness it would bring to you. This feeling of joy helps you manifest the dream. This positive energy helps you attract your dreams.

3  **Create a vision board.** Put photos of your passions, hopes and dreams up on a board where you'll see them every day. This is a crazy-powerful tool. Right now, I'm dreaming of health, happiness and freedom, along with a family of my own, a house on the street I grew up on, a bigger JSHealth community and a wall of my vitamins in pharmacies across Australia and the US. Those dreams are on my vision board, and I smile whenever I walk past it.

# 14 Try not to force it

Finally, don't tell yourself you need to be happier or that you should be more positive, as this signals to the brain that you're not happy or positive. Often, this piles on the pressure and stress, and won't make you feel any better.

Instead, take small steps to change your mindset each day. Focus on your blessings and the parts of your life that bring you joy. Be empathetic and kind. Soon enough, your mindset will shift.

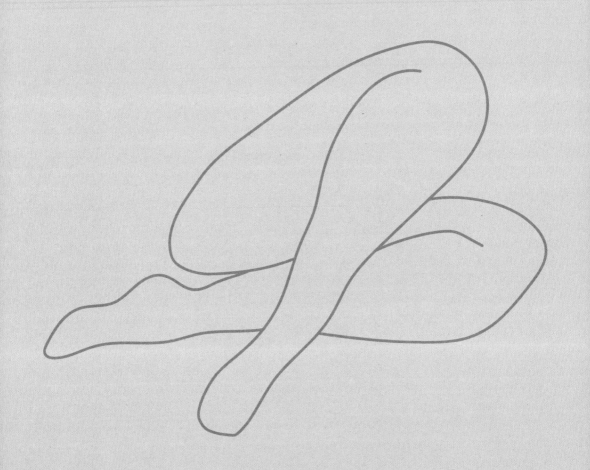

# 3

# Eat all of the macronutrients

---

*When I don't eat a balanced diet, I end up craving sugar, overeating or bingeing.*

# I don't believe in cutting out food groups

As a nutritionist, I see so many people who've experimented with their diets over the years – cutting out one food group after another in their quest to reach their perfect weight. And as a recovered fad dieter myself, I've been there! I eliminated every food group at some point as I followed the trends. I was vegan one month, paleo the next and then on the Atkins diet after that ... These diets have completely different philosophies! Each has its own rules about restricting carbs, protein and fat, but they have one thing in common: each of them restricts food groups.

After trying every fad diet, I was left beyond confused. And it's no wonder – every diet told me something different. Wait, which food groups was I meant to avoid? What foods could I actually eat? I had no idea! I was afraid to go with my gut and eat what felt right.

So let me teach you how to build a balanced, satiating meal using all of the food groups. We need to support our bodies by feeding them with the nutrients they need to thrive. It's as simple as that. If you don't eat nourishing, nutrient-dense foods, you'll feel unsatisfied, and this often leads to overeating, low energy or making poor food choices. On the other hand, if you know how to create a healthy plate each and every time you eat, you're be more likely to keep making healthy choices.

I believe we should be eating all of the food groups. That's not to say it's a free-for-all: I think we should enjoy the best sources of each food group in balanced amounts – and I'll show you what I mean by that in a minute.

By following this way of eating, you'll be fuller for longer, your energy will stay stable, and your cravings will become a thing of the past. This makes healthy eating enjoyable and effortless over time. Exciting, right?

In this chapter, I'm going to walk you through the macronutrients, and why they're so important. You'll learn that building a healthy plate isn't hard, and that little tweaks go a long way.

## Meet the macros

The term macronutrients (aka 'macros') gets tossed around a lot in the health world, but many people don't understand what it means, or why macronutrients are so important.

Macronutrients are the main nutrients we get from food. There are four macronutrients, and we need to eat each of them at every meal in order for our body to function at its best.

$$\frac{\text{Carbohydrates} + \textit{fibre} + \text{Protein} +}{\text{Fat} = 4 \text{ } \textit{Macronutrient} \text{ groups}}$$

Each macronutrient is essential, and has its own specific role to play in the body. A balanced plate includes all four of them. These macronutrients are the most satiating of all nutrients. If you're avoiding one of them (like carbs), this could be the reason you're overeating in the afternoon or at dinner, or why you're prone to late-night snacking.

 ## Carbohydrates

Carbohydrates include foods such as breads, pastas and grains, as well as fruit, veggies, beans and legumes. Most diets are designed to avoid carbs. But carbs aren't the devil! As a nutritionist, I believe we should eat carbs – just the right kinds. Carbs are actually the body's main source of energy. Without them, our energy dips and we can feel sluggish and experience brain fog.

Since carbs are quickly converted by the body into glucose, they're also the easiest macronutrient to absorb. However, to stay energised throughout the day, it's better for our bodies to absorb glucose slowly. That's why I recommend one serving of 'complex' or slow-releasing carbs rather than 'simple' carbs at each meal. (See the tables on pages 45 and 238.)

Focus on getting your carbohydrate fix from fruit, pulses, healthy grains and starchy veggies (like sweet potato). From my personal and in-clinic experience, these are better for energy and gut health. On the other hand, many people find gluten-containing grains harder to digest.

 ## Fibre

Fibre is probably the most underrated macronutrient because people a) aren't getting enough of it, and b) don't realise how important it is. You may already know that fibre is in charge of keeping the digestive system moving, but did you know that it's also responsible for soaking up excess toxins in the gut? I find not many people do! It's important to go to the toilet once a day for the healthy release of toxins, so think of fibre as a broom for your digestive system. It stabilises blood sugar, lowers cholesterol, removes excess hormones from the body and reduces the risk of colon cancer. It also enhances long-term weight loss.

There are two types of fibre: soluble and insoluble. **Soluble fibre** attracts water and turns into gel in the digestive system. It keeps your blood glucose levels in check, and helps you to feel full. Good sources of soluble fibre include oat bran, barley, nuts, seeds, beans, lentils and psyllium

# QUIT DIETING AND TRY MY BALANCED APPROACH TO FOOD INSTEAD

✳ Half your plate:
green, leafy vegetables
(the more colorful and green,
the better!)

✳ Palm-sized
portion of protein
with every meal

✳ Enjoy a portion of good
fats with every meal
(e.g. extra-virgin olive oil dressing,
avocado, nuts, seeds or tahini.)

✳ A quarter of your
plate: slow-releasing
carbohydrates
(e.g. brown rice, beans, quinoa,
lentils or sweet potato.)

✳
Reduce
refined sugar
and simple
carbs

✳
Limit dairy
to two
portions
a day

✳
Sip on one
coffee a day
before 10 am

✳
If you eat red
meat, limit
your intake
to two serves
per week

✳
Indulge in
moderation
twice a week

husk. **Insoluble fibre** adds bulk to the stool and helps food to pass more easily, making it great for those who suffer from constipation. Wholegrains, wheat bran, rice bran, fruit and vegetable skins, nuts, seeds and legumes are all packed with insoluble fibre.

Aim to eat 30–40 grams of fibre a day. For an easy fix of fibre, add 1 or 2 tablespoons of chia seeds or ground flaxseed to your breakfast every day, enjoy two high-fibre crackers with your lunchtime salad, and include half a plate of colourful veggies with each meal. You can find these at most grocery or health-food stores.

If you eat these foods, your bowels should start working more regularly.

 ## Protein

Protein is important for all of our cells and systems. It's vital for keeping our organs, muscles, skin, hair, nails and blood healthy and strong. It also speeds up our metabolism, lifts our energy, helps us to feel full and produces healthy hormones. It helps us to build lean body mass, which burns fat very effectively. Protein also helps to boost mental clarity and productivity, as most of the neurotransmitters in the brain are made up of amino acids, the building blocks of protein.

Every meal and snack should include a palm-sized portion of protein. If you're training a lot, you may need to increase your protein even more.

 ## Fats (the good ones)

Good fats are vital for health and wellbeing. They produce hormones, protect organs and reduce inflammation in the body. If you eat good fats, your skin, hormones and waistline will thank you for it. Yes, really! You'll also be rewarded with healthy heart and brain function, lower blood pressure, and balanced hormones. Fats can even help with PMS! The essential fatty acids in good fats (omega-3s and omegas-6s) can also improve our skin and mood, and keep us feeling fuller for longer.

Trans fats are the ones you want to avoid. Found in almost all processed, packaged, fried and baked foods, trans fats are the result of adding hydrogen to liquid vegetable oils to make them more solid. Because they are an industrially made product, the body doesn't recognise them or know how to break them down. Over time, trans fats can build up in the system and, in some cases, start to cling to artery walls, causing problems like heart disease and increased cholesterol.

Finally, after years of 'fat talk' (aka scare tactics) in the media, we now know that eating fat won't make you fat. You'll only store fat if you overeat it or eat the wrong kinds. So enjoy one serving of good fat per meal.

### Refined oils to avoid

You also want to avoid vegetable and seed oils such as safflower oil, peanut oil, soybean oil, canola oil, sunflower oil and cottonseed oil. These oils are often refined, processed and high in omega-6, which is fine in small amounts but is linked to inflammation and disease when the balance is out. The Western diet in particular has an imbalance of omega-3s and -6s compared with other diets in the world, and that's an issue. A good omega-6 to -3 ratio is 4:1, but ask any anti-ageing expert, and they'll tell you to reduce it to 1:1. To put this in context, the average American eats anywhere from 12:1 to 25:1.

My nutrition guide on page 238 outlines macros and portion sizes in detail. But here's a cheat sheet for quick reference as a starting point to get your head around macros.

## Macros at a glance

| Macro | Eat these | Avoid these |
|---|---|---|
| Carbs | √ Slow-releasing carbs: wholegrains, rye bread, brown or basmati rice, sweet potato and quinoa. | X Simple carbs: white bread, white rice, white pasta, white crackers, cereal and refined sugar. |
| Fibre | √ Oats, dark leafy greens, fruits, nuts, flaxseed, chia seeds and psyllium husk. | X Processed and packaged foods. |
| Protein | √ High-quality animal protein (which is easier for the body to digest) such as lean organic chicken or turkey, grass-fed beef, organic eggs, and sustainably sourced seafood and fish.<br><br>There are plenty of vegetarian protein sources (like tempeh, beans, legumes and nuts), but you may find them harder to digest. | X Deli meats (like salami), caged eggs, farmed fish and poor-quality chicken and meat. |
| Fats | √ Good fats: avocado, oily fish, flaxseed, nuts, seeds and extra-virgin olive oil. | X Refined vegetable or seed oils. Trans fats found in: vegetable shortening, pre-made snacks and foods, baked foods and fried foods. |

# A DAY OF BALANCED EATING

---

Live the healthy life, and you'll get to eat every 2–4 hours. This will boost your energy levels, mood and mental clarity, and ensure you don't get 'hangry' or succumb to sugar cravings. This is what your meals should look like.

## Breakfast *7–10 am*

Eating a wholesome breakfast is a huge part of the health equation. It kickstarts your digestion and metabolism, and feeds your body with the vitamins and minerals it needs to perform. Please don't skip it or you'll set yourself up for a day on the blood sugar roller-coaster, and trigger the release of stress hormones like cortisol. Try to eat within 1 hour of waking, and always include protein and fat. Studies show that those who eat breakfast manage their weight easier. See Chapter 4 for breakfasts.

## Snack *11 am (optional)*

I'm a BIG believer in the importance of snacks. Mid-morning is a great time to have a green juice and a small snack. If you look at my Instagram feed, you'll see that I always have a nutritious snack between main meals – and it's not just because I love eating! I say this snack is optional as some people are simply not hungry at this time of day. Tune in to your appetite. If you're craving fruit like a green apple or berries, have it for your morning snack rather than your afternoon snack. See pages 176–77 for my favourite protein-rich snacks.

## Lunch *12.30–1.30 pm*

Lunch does more than just break up a work day. It ensures your body slowly releases energy for the rest of the day, and prevents the dreaded 3 pm slump.

For lunch, combine dark leafy greens with one or two servings of protein, one portion of good fat and one portion of starchy veggies (such as sweet potato), and gluten-free grains or legumes for the fibre and nutrients. Most people feel fuller when they add a portion of fat to their lunch. It does wonders for energy levels and banishes sugar cravings in the afternoon.

The options for creating a balanced plate are endless! You'll never get bored. Check out the meal builder on pages 48–49 for some easy ideas. Better yet, print it out and keep it in your kitchen for those days you need a little inspiration.

## Snack *4–5 pm*

An afternoon snack may not sound revolutionary, but I find that many women skip it because they're scared of the extra calories. However it's one of the key habits that supports my healthy lifestyle, and I'd love for you to try it. So reach for a protein-rich snack in the late afternoon. This will keep your blood sugars stable until dinner, and help to combat overeating in the evening. If you're trying to reduce sugar cravings, please avoid fruit in the afternoon as, from experience, it can trigger sugar cravings after dinner. See pages 176–77 for my go-to afternoon snacks.

## Dinner *7 pm*

A delicious dinner is one of the best parts of living the healthy life. If you have satiating meals all day, there's no need to go overboard with dinner. In Chapter 8, I show you quick and easy meals that tick all the macronutrient boxes. In the evening, the body is winding down, preparing for sleep, so it's your job to feed it a small dose of nutrient-dense food before it 'fasts' overnight. When preparing dinner, think protein with non-starchy veggies and lots of greens. You can also add a portion of healthy carbs, such as sweet potato, quinoa or brown rice, to your dinner two to four times a week. Some people feel better when they don't eat heavy starches at night, but if you love them, enjoy them! I suggest trying to eat 1–2 hours before bed for optimal digestion.

## Post-dinner *8.30 pm*

Do you have a sweet tooth? I believe in moderation, so I encourage you to treat yourself twice a week after dinner. If you can slow down and savour a couple of bliss balls, two squares of dark chocolate or a raw chocolate mousse, it will be satiating. You'll find my favourite healthy treats on page 217.

Then, sip on a cup of herbal tea to digest and calm your body. I love chamomile tea or decaf chai tea with vanilla stevia and almond milk – it hits the spot!

### Indulging without guilt

My approach is built on balance, not extremes. I'm all for eating everything in moderation – and that includes treats! I explore this in Chapter 11, but for now know that indulgence actually helps you to stay on track. It encourages you to have a healthy relationship with food, and be consistent with your food choices. Treat yourself twice a week to a healthy (or not-so-healthy) treat. Enjoy it without guilt, then move on.

# Mix-and-match meal builder

This is my formula for making breakfast, lunch or dinner. Once you start cooking at home, you'll naturally reach for the ingredients you love! Healthy cooking doesn't need to be complicated, so stick to easy methods, such as steaming, sautéing, roasting or pan-frying.

## 1 Choose a fresh base: 2–3 cups of *fresh* or cooked *leafy greens*

| rocket | iceberg lettuce | baby spinach leaves | cos lettuce | mixed lettuce salad leaves | kale, torn leaves |

## 2 Add 1 cup of tasty colourful *veggies* (raw or cooked)

| fresh baby tomatoes | cucumber | cabbage (green or red) | carrot | red onion |

| broccoli | cauliflower | carrot chips | zucchini | eggplant |

## 3 Add 150 g (or a palm-sized portion) of cooked *protein*

| chicken or turkey breast | fish (white fish, salmon, barramundi, snapper) | 1 or 2 eggs | grass-fed beef or lamb | ½ cup veggie protein (lentils, beans or pulses) | 100 g tempeh or tofu |

# 4 Add ½ cup of complex or *slow-releasing cooked carb*

| pumpkin | sweet potato | beetroot | basmati or brown rice | organic lentils or beans | quinoa | brown rice or mung bean pasta |

# 5 Add about 2 tablespoons of *good fats*

¼–½ an avocado | drizzle of flaxseed oil, cold-pressed extra-virgin olive oil or hulled tahini | sprinkle of roasted almonds or pepitas | cook with either coconut oil or cold-pressed extra-virgin olive oil

# 6 Add ⅓ cup (80 ml) of *healthy dressing* or *sauce*

Teriyaki dressing (page 118) | Moroccan tahini dressing (page 119) | My Four-step lemon and herb dressing (page 118) | hummus

# 7 Add extra *yumminess* with a sprinkle or drizzle of these ingredients

nutritional yeast | curry powder | red or green onion | sea salt | dried chilli flakes | lemon or lime juice | fresh herbs (basil, parsley, mint, chives, coriander)

### Japanese salmon and cauliflower rice bowl

Fill your bowl with 2–3-cups kale, sautéed in extra-virgin olive oil, 1 cup cauliflower rice, sautéed in extra-virgin olive oil and curry spice, 150–200 g salmon fillet, marinated in Teriyaki dressing (page 118), ½ cup baked sweet potato, and sea salt and freshly ground black pepper. Drizzle over lemon juice and extra-virgin olive oil to serve.

### Egg and greens bowl

Fill your bowl with 2–3 cups baby kale, 1 cup cauliflower rice, sautéed in extra-virgin olive oil and garlic, 1 cup steamed cauliflower, 2 boiled eggs, ½ cup baked pumpkin, ¼ avocado and sea salt and freshly ground black pepper.

## Healthy chicken teriyaki bowl

Fill your bowl with 2–3 cups rocket and/or spinach, 1 cup steamed broccoli, 150 g grilled chicken breast, ½ cup brown rice, ¼ avocado, Teriyaki dressing (page 118) and sea salt and freshly ground black pepper.

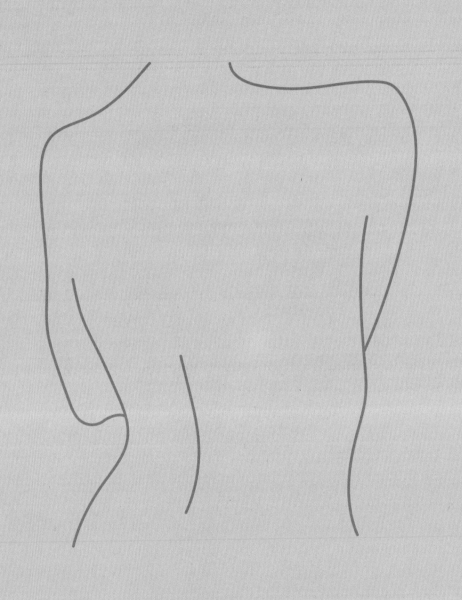

# 4

# Set up a nourishing morning routine

---

*I have a non-negotiable morning routine, which includes moving my body. This routine is the cheapest, most powerful part of my healthy life.*

# Picture this ...

You wake up and immediately reach for your phone. You start scrolling through social media, bleary-eyed and lying in bed (hello, comparison and anxiety). You check your emails (hello, stress), read messages from friends and family (hello, overwhelm) and you review your calendar for the day (hello, nerves). A million thoughts are now racing through your mind – and you've only been awake for 3 minutes!

So you rush to the bathroom. You do your business in a hurry (hello, compromised digestion). You consider exercising, but tell yourself there's no time. Or you throw yourself into an intense workout and hate it.

You make breakfast, but only if you have time and there's food in the fridge. And you eat on the move (hello, indigestion!).

The reason for all this rushing is simple: you have too much to do!

By the time you get to the office, you're anxious, overwhelmed or scattered – or all three – and you probably don't even realise it. Does this sound familiar?

Starting our mornings without giving ourselves a chance to adjust to the day isn't healthy for the mind, body or spirit.

But there's good news ...

**Creating a _calmer_ and _healthier_ morning routine will _change your life._**

By that, I mean implementing a set of daily rituals that focus on YOUR wellbeing and not the demands of the outside world. This will drastically improve your mood,

energy and anxiety, and encourage you to make healthier choices. Your morning has a ripple effect on the rest of your day.

Many of the most successful people in the world have morning routines they swear by. They call this the 'millionaire morning'. They are committed to carving out some time for themselves – and they cherish it. This sets them up for a productive and powerful day, and it motivates them, both mentally and physically.

A good routine is all about mirroring our natural circadian rhythm. We're not medieval farmers, so we don't wake up at dawn and go to bed at sunset anymore, but we can do our best to replicate this in modern life by waking up slooowly. And this process doesn't have to be a big thing. If you can just be selfish for a few minutes each morning, it will make a world of difference.

So in this chapter, I'm going to share my morning routine for self-care, good health, less stress and better digestion. But before I do, I want to urge you to stop doing my morning no-noes starting tomorrow!

## Morning no-noes

X   Looking at your phone or social media as soon as you open your eyes. Invest in an old-school alarm clock!

X   Skipping breakfast. Please eat! More on this on page 59.

X   Flooding your body with caffeine, and caffeine only. (You can still have it, but just maybe not as much as you're drinking now!)

Set up a nourishing morning routine

*(p.s. It is worth copying!)*

# MY POWERFUL MORNING ROUTINE

I've created a simple morning routine that keeps me on track for the rest of the day. When I wake up, I focus on myself for 10–30 minutes. Some days I have more time than others. I don't put pressure on myself; I just make sure I dedicate some time to me.

This routine has evolved into a beautiful ritual, and I actually look forward to it every day. Why? It puts me in a positive frame of mind and increases my endorphins (the happy hormones). It has also reduced my anxiety in a major way.

There's no pressure to follow my routine to a tee; don't feel you have to do all the things I do every day. Just do what you can with the time you have. I simply want you to become more aware of your morning (and your stress triggers), and try to tweak a few aspects of it so you begin your day on a healthy note. For example, if you find it difficult to workout on an empty stomach, try eating fruit, eggs a smoothie or a healthy bar prior to working out.

I want to point out that a great morning routine starts the night before. You won't feel motivated to spring out of bed if you've stayed up too late scrolling on your phone or glued to the TV screen. To clear away the stresses of the day, see my relaxing night-time routine in detail in Chapter 7.

## Wake up

I wake up at 6.30 or 7 am and take ten deep belly breaths to calm my nervous system. Since there's no phone near me, I spend a few minutes thinking of, and visualising, all of the things, people and situations I'm grateful for. And then I verbally thank the universe for them. For instance, you could say:

- 'Thank you for my loving family/ friends/partner.'
- 'Thank you for my beautiful home.'
- 'Thank you for my strength.'

This keeps me grounded and allows me to start my day with a positive mindset.

## Water

I head to the kitchen and sip a big glass of room-temperature water with a squeeze of lemon. I pop a 50-billion strain probiotic to heal and seal my gut.

## Meditation

If I have a little more time, I meditate for 5–10 minutes, or I simply sit in a quiet place and breathe deeply for 5 minutes. This doesn't happen every day, but when it does, my mind feels so much clearer.

# Coffee

At this point, I'll enjoy an espresso with a dash of milk. I drink my coffee before 10 am and stick to the JSHealth guideline of one a day for cortisol balance, better sleep and steady energy – not to mention fewer sugar cravings!

# Workout

I do a 30-minute 'body love' workout of my choice. I tune in to my body and find a workout that matches my mood. Usually it's yoga, HIIT (high-intensity interval training) on the treadmill or a walk outside (see page 59 for my Body Blitz gym workout). On some days I and don't have the time or energy to exercise – and that's okay. I let it go and aim to fit in a 15-minute walk before or after dinner. I don't feel guilty about it. Rest days are healthy, and necessary. Be kind.

# Breakfast

Within an hour of working out, I whip up a wholesome breakfast. This is the optimal timeframe for blood sugar control and muscle recovery. I sit down, eat mindfully and don't look at my phone. My breakfast contains slow-releasing carbs, protein, fibre and fat – essentials for energy, mood and weight balance.

# Vitamins

I take my JSHealth vitamins. These are designed for stress management and better skin, energy, focus, digestive and hair health, and hundreds of people have had phenomenal results on them. See jshealthvitamins.com for more info.

# Water bottle

I fill up a stainless-steel bottle with filtered water and add 2 tablespoons of apple cider vinegar (ACV) so it's diluted and easy to drink. ACV is brilliant for sugar cravings, digestion and overall gut health. I put my water bottle on my desk or wherever I am for the day, and every time I look at it, I take a sip.

# Ready to go!

Now, I'm ready for a productive day. I'm calm and happy, so I open my computer and check my messages and emails.

Can you choose one or two things from this routine to try tomorrow? I'm all about taking small steps to create incredible changes in the mind and body.

# Move your body!

After you've woken up slowly is a great time to get some exercise. I prefer exercising in the morning. Working out increases adrenaline and energy, which is perfect when you're starting your day. Exercising in the evening can mess with your sleep; that's why I stick to walks and yin yoga at night.

For good energy, weight balance and body love, I believe we should exercise with kindness and in ways we enjoy. That's more important than intensity.

From clinical experience, I can tell you that intense exercise doesn't work for everyone. If it works for you, go ahead. However, if you've been pushing yourself at the gym but still aren't seeing results, it might be time for a new approach.

My movement principles are kind, gentle and moderate. I've met so many women who've adopted this philosophy and reported feeling better than ever. They're enjoying having more energy, deeper sleep and looser clothes. Now it's your turn!

But first, let me tell you why I follow this philosophy. When I exercise to the extreme, I feel tired and I'm desperately hungry all day. I also find it harder to maintain my weight. It's just what happens to me, based on my genes and the makeup of my nervous system.

I used to exercise to burn off calories, slim down and tone up. I wasn't working out to feel good – I was working out to look good. Now I see exercise as an act of self-love. It gives my body a boost, supports my mental health, and lifts my energy and mood. I put my body first and listen to it. If I wake up feeling tired, I rest without guilt. If I'm not in the mood for HIIT, I go to yoga or walk outside instead. I don't force it and I don't overdo it.

Remember, everyone is different. So we have to tune in to our own bodies and figure out what works for us. In saying that, I'll outline the movement protocol that has worked so well for the thousands of women who follow the JSHealth program.

- **Move your body for 30–40 minutes a day in a way you love.** That's all you need to reap the benefits of exercise. No more hellish bootcamps (unless you like them, of course).
- **Mix it up.** I do a mix of yoga, Pilates, walking and HIIT. The body loves variety; ask any personal trainer and they'll tell you this is one of the best ways to get results. It's important for us to exercise in gentle ways, which is why I incorporate yoga and Pilates.
- **Don't underestimate the power of restorative exercise.** Think yin yoga and walks in nature. These are amazing forms of stress relief, and the mind and body crave them. I look forward to my yin classes each week, and I walk outside as much as I can!
- **Enjoy one or two rest days a week.** The body needs rest as much as it needs movement – don't feel guilty!

## Should you eat before you exercise?

If you exercise in the morning, you can enjoy a coffee pre-workout. Otherwise, I find it's best to exercise on an empty stomach because your body will use stored glycogen as a fuel source, which makes it easier to burn fat. So if you work out on an empty stomach, you can potentially burn more fat. After your workout, try to eat a protein-rich breakfast within 30 minutes. This replenishes your energy stores and feeds your muscles.

However, if you find you can't workout on an empty stomach please eat first. And speaking of breakfast ...

# *Activity*

## MY BODY BLITZ GYM WORKOUT

This 30-minute workout is quick, easy and engages all major muscles. I do it two to three times each week.

**Stretch**
Work through a few yoga poses to loosen up the body and increase flexibility.

**Cardio**
High-intensity interval training (HIIT) on the treadmill for 20 minutes. This involves jogging for 5 minutes, then sprinting for 1 minute.

**Strength**
Aim to repeat this circuit 3 times. It's okay if you need to build up to that. As always, when you're working out, focus on your form rather than on speed.

- 20 triceps dips
- 20 sit-ups or push-ups
- 1-minute plank
- 15–20 weighted squats (hold a 2–5 kg weight in each hand) or 10 burpees

## We have to talk about breakfast

Throughout my career as a nutritionist, the most common thing I hear from clients is, 'I don't eat breakfast,' and when I ask them why, they usually tell me it's because they don't have time, or they don't feel like it. But eating a wholesome breakfast is a huge part of the health equation so try to eat within 1 hour of waking. Flick to page page 46 to see how eating breakfast kickstarts your digestion and metabolism.

# Breakfast stations

To solve the 'no time for breakfast' issue – and to cut down on the amount of time I spend in the kitchen – I've become the master of fast, no-fuss breakfasts. I'm also passionate about making sure my breakfasts have the right balance of nutrients, because what you eat in the morning can affect your food choices and energy levels for the rest of the day.

After lots of experimenting, I've narrowed down my breakfast go-to's to three quick, easy and nutrient-dense options: an oat/granola bowl, an egg bowl, and a smoothie. I literally have a station set up for each of these dishes in my kitchen. This makes my mornings SO much easier and it's perfect for those who truly don't have time. You can take them with you to work or school.

Each of these options contains all of the essential macronutrients: a portion of protein, slow-releasing carbs, good fat and fibre. As you might remember from Chapter 3, these macronutrients work to fill you up, release energy slowly, reduce sugar cravings and suit every mood.

BREAKFAST STATION ONE
## Smoothie station

A smoothie is the perfect grab-and-go breakfast to cool you down on a warm day. Always be prepared by keeping these ingredients on your kitchen bench.

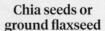

**Chia seeds or ground flaxseed**

- A good blender
- Pea/whey protein powder or LSA mix
- Chia seeds or ground flaxseed
- Ripe bananas (you can also slice these and store in the freezer)
- Almond butter or peanut butter
- Sweeteners: cinnamon, stevia or maple syrup
- Toppings: a bowl of goji berries or nuts and seeds

From the fridge/freezer: almond milk, ice cubes, and frozen banana/berries.

PROTEIN    FIBRE    CARBS    GOOD FAT

Cinnamon, stevia or maple syrup

Protein powder or LSA mix

Almond butter or peanut butter

Almond milk

Goji berries

Frozen berries

Ripe bananas

# Oat/granola bowl station

If you wake up feeling like something sweet, there's nothing tastier than an oat/granola bowl. Pop the ingredients below in an easy accessible place to make mornings quick, easy and healthy!

- Organic rolled oats or my Cinnamon–chai coconut granola (page 74)
- Toppings: goji berries, mixed nuts and seeds, and chia seeds or ground flaxseed
- Ripe bananas
- Sweeteners: cinnamon, honey or maple syrup

From the fridge/freezer: almond milk, Greek yoghurt and berries.

**PROTEIN    FIBRE    CARBS    GOOD FAT**

Almond milk and Greek yoghurt

Goji berries, mixed nuts and seeds, or ground flaxseed

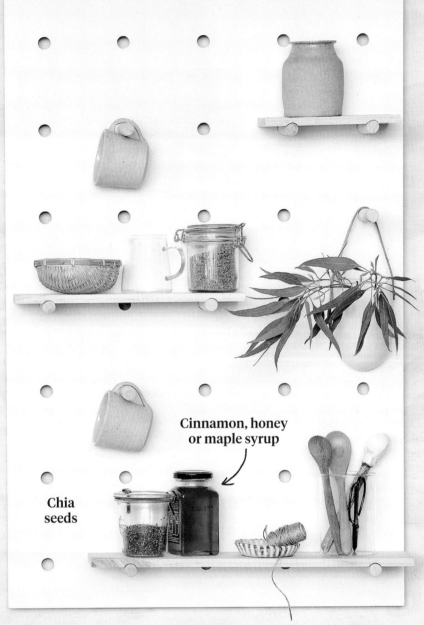

Cinnamon, honey
or maple syrup

Chia
seeds

Organic rolled oats or
Cinnamon-chai coconut
granola *page 74*

Ripe bananas

Berries

# Egg station

Keep these goodies on your kitchen bench so you'll always be able to whip up a nourishing omelette or some scrambled, poached or boiled eggs.

- Olive oil  or olive oil spray and ripe avocado
- Himalayan salt
- Chilli flakes
- Fresh herbs: basil, parsley and dill
- Fresh sourdough  , rye or my Cauliflower and seed bread (page 124)

From the fridge: organic eggs

**PROTEIN**    **FIBRE**    **CARBS**    **GOOD FAT**

Fresh basil

Organic eggs

Chilli flakes

Fresh
parsley

Olive oil or
olive oil spray

Fresh sourdough,
rye or my Cauliflower
and seed bread
*page 124*

Ripe
avocado

Fresh dill

# How to build an egg bowl

Ask anyone who knows me and they'll tell you I love egg bowls! They're versatile and quick and easy to whip up with whatever I have in the fridge. You could have one every day for lunch or dinner, and switch up the ingredients every time.

## 1 Go-to greens

Sauté 2 cups of greens (such as baby spinach, kale, silverbeet, English spinach or Asian greens) in 1 tablespoon of coconut oil or cold-pressed extra-virgin olive oil – and add to your bowl.

## 2 Eggs

Cook 2 eggs your favourite way – boiled (hard or soft), poached or scrambled – and then add them to the greens.

## 3 Grains or a starchy veggie

Top with a grain or starchy vegetable such as ½ cup cooked quinoa or brown or basmati rice; or ½ cup roasted sweet potato or pumpkin.

## 4 Nourishing fats

¼–½ avocado, served as is in the skin, or smashed or sliced.

## 5 Dress it up

Drizzle with 2–3 tablespoons of pesto or tahini or a dollop of hummus.

## 6 Add a little crunch

Sprinkle with a small handful of nuts (whole natural almonds, walnuts, pecans) and seeds (pepitas, sunflower or sesame) or raw sprouts.

**Now sit down and tuck in to the bowl of goodness you've just built!**

# Almond butter dream smoothie

GF  DF  VEG  VEGAN

**SERVES** 1
**PREP** 10 MINUTES

---

135 g (1 cup) small ice cubes
250 ml (1 cup) Almond, coconut
    and vanilla milk (page 110)
25–30 g (2 tablespoons) vanilla
    pea protein powder
1 tablespoon almond butter
1 tablespoon chia seeds
1 teaspoon ground cinnamon,
    plus an extra pinch to serve
½ frozen banana
1 pitted medjool date
pinch of sea salt

1   Place all the ingredients
    in an upright blender
    and blend until
    completely smooth.

2   Serve immediately
    with extra cinnamon
    sprinkled on top.

# Peanut butter-choc smoothie jar

**DF**   **VEG**   **VEGAN**

**SERVES** 1
**PREP** 15 MINUTES

½ cup (30 g) Cinnamon-chai
    coconut granola (page 74)
½ frozen banana
135 g (1 cup) small ice cubes
25–30g (2 tablespoons)
    chocolate pea protein powder
1 tablespoon peanut butter
    (crunchy or smooth), plus
    1 teaspoon extra to serve
1 tablespoon chia seeds
125 ml (½ cup) coconut water
cacao nibs, to serve

1   Spoon the granola into
    a wide-mouthed jar.

2   Place the banana, ice,
    protein powder, peanut
    butter, chia seeds and
    coconut water in an
    upright blender and
    blend until completely
    smooth and thick. Add
    1–2 tablespoons of
    water to loosen slightly
    if needed, but you
    want it to have a thick,
    spoonable consistency.

3   Spoon this mixture
    over the granola in the
    jar, piling it high. Dollop
    the extra peanut butter
    on top then serve
    immediately, sprinkled
    with cacao nibs.

# Almond butter and banana protein muffins

**GF** **DF** **VEG**

**SERVES** 10
**PREP** 15 MINUTES
**COOKING** 15 MINUTES
+ COOLING TIME

———

2 bananas (about 200 g), peeled
    and mashed
2 large eggs, whisked
1 teaspoon vanilla bean powder
90 g (⅓ cup) almond butter, plus
    extra to serve
90 g (¾ cup) LSA mix
1 teaspoon baking powder
chia seeds, to serve
pepitas, to serve

1 Preheat the oven to 180°C (160°C fan-forced). Line ten holes of a 12-hole, ⅓-cup capacity muffin pan with paper cases.

2 Place all the ingredients in a bowl and mix until well combined.

3 Divide the mixture evenly between the prepared muffin holes then bake for 15 minutes, or until they are cooked through and golden. Insert a skewer into one of the muffins – if it comes out clean, the muffins are ready. If not, bake for another minute or until done.

4 Remove the muffins from the oven and leave in the pan for 5 minutes before transferring to a wire rack to cool completely.

5 Serve topped with extra almond butter and sprinkled with chia seeds and pepitas.

# Raspberry chia pudding

**GF  VEG**

**SERVES** 1
**PREP** 10 MINUTES
+ OVERNIGHT CHILLING

—

60 g (½ cup) fresh raspberries
45 g (¼ cup) chia seeds
2 teaspoons vanilla bean powder
1 tablespoon golden flaxmeal
1 tablespoon pure maple syrup
250 ml (1 cup) milk of choice
   (pages 110–11)
40 g (¼ cup) whole natural
   almonds, roughly chopped
½ banana, sliced
good pinch of ground cinnamon
a few fresh blueberries
1 tablespoon Greek yoghurt

1   Place the raspberries in a small serving bowl and use a fork to mash them well. Add the chia seeds, vanilla bean powder, flaxmeal, maple syrup and milk, and whisk together with the fork until everything is well combined and any lumps of powder have been broken up.

2   Cover and refrigerate overnight, or until set.

3   Top the chia pudding with the chopped almonds, sliced banana, cinnamon, blueberries and Greek yoghurt then serve right away.

## Make it dairy-free and vegan ...

By using one of my homemade milks on pages 110–11 and removing the Greek yoghurt.

# Ricotta and tomato omelette with basil

**DF  VEG**

**SERVES** 1
**PREP** 10 MINUTES
**COOK** 5 MINUTES

—

1 tablespoon coconut oil
2 large eggs, whisked
50 g fresh ricotta
4 cherry tomatoes, halved
½ handful of basil leaves
1 slice of sourdough bread,
   toasted
sea salt and freshly ground
   black pepper
pinch of dried chilli flakes,
   to serve (optional)

1   Heat the oil in a small non-stick frying pan over medium heat. Add the eggs and swirl them around gently so they coat the base of the pan. Cook, shaking the pan occasionally, for 2–3 minutes, or until the egg is firmly set around the edges and softly set in the middle.

2   Crumble the ricotta over the omelette and add the tomato. Cook, untouched, for another minute or until almost set in the centre.

3   Sprinkle over the basil leaves and, using a soft spatula, gently fold one half of the omelette over the other.

4   Slide the omelette out of the pan and onto a serving plate, then season well with salt and pepper. Serve hot sprinkled with the chilli flakes, if desired, with the toasted sourdough alongside.

Raspberry chia pudding

# Sticky date pudding breakfast oats

**VEG**

**SERVES** 1
**PREP** 10 MINUTES
**COOK** 15 MINUTES

———

50 g (½ cup) rolled oats
125 ml (½ cup) milk of choice
    (pages 110–11)
4 large fresh medjool dates,
    pitted and chopped
1 tablespoon tahini, plus
    1 teaspoon extra to serve
2 tablespoons Greek yoghurt
    or coconut yoghurt, to serve
pure maple syrup, to serve

1   Place the oats, milk, half the dates, tahini and 185 ml (¾ cup) water in a small saucepan over medium heat. Cook, stirring constantly, until the mixture comes to a simmer.

2   Reduce the heat to the lowest setting possible and cook for 12–15 minutes, stirring occasionally and adding a little more water if needed, until the oats are soft and the mixture has thickened.

3   Spoon the mixture into a serving bowl. Top with the yoghurt, remaining dates and extra tahini. Serve warm with a little drizzle of maple syrup.

# Cinnamon-chai coconut granola

**DF    VEG  VEGAN**

**SERVES** 4
**PREP** 15 MINUTES
**COOK** 20 MINUTES
+ COOLING TIME

———

3 tablespoons coconut oil,
    melted
2 tablespoons pure maple syrup
1 teaspoon vanilla bean powder
2 teaspoons ground cinnamon
1 teaspoon ground cardamom
1 teaspoon ground ginger
65 g (½ cup) chopped mixed
    nuts such as whole natural
    almonds, walnuts or pecans
80 g (½ cup) mixed seeds such
    as sunflower, pepita or chia
50 g (1 cup) flaked coconut
100 g (1 cup) rolled oats

1   Preheat the oven to 180°C (160°C fan-forced). Line a large baking tray with non-stick baking paper.

2   Place all of the ingredients together in a large bowl and toss well to combine. Make sure everything is coated evenly in the melted oil and spices.

3   Spread this mixture evenly over the prepared tray and bake for 10 minutes, then use a spatula or wooden spoon to turn the mixture over and move everything around the tray. Bake for 5–8 minutes more, or until the granola is evenly golden. Remove from the oven and leave to cool completely on the tray.

4   Store in an airtight container at room temperature for up to 2 weeks. When ready to serve, scoop ½-cup measures of granola into a bowl, add 125 ml (½ cup) of your milk of choice (page 110–11) and top with ½ cup of your favourite seasonal fruits, such as sliced banana, fresh berries or sliced kiwi fruit.

**Sticky date pudding
breakfast oats**

# Mushrooms and greens with egg

**DF**   **VEG**

**SERVES** 1
**PREP** 15 MINUTES
**COOK** 10 MINUTES

————

1 tablespoon coconut oil
150 g button mushrooms,
    cleaned and halved
1 zucchini, sliced into rounds
good pinch of dried mixed herbs
1 garlic clove, crushed
1 cup torn kale leaves or kalette
1 cup (firmly packed) baby
    spinach leaves
1 large egg
sea salt and freshly ground
    black pepper
1 slice of sourdough, toasted

1   Heat the oil in a medium non-stick frying pan over high heat. Add the mushrooms and zucchini and cook, stirring occasionally, for 3 minutes or until the vegetables are starting to soften and turn golden.

2   Reduce the heat to medium–low and add the dried mixed herbs, garlic, kale, spinach and 2 tablespoons of water. Cook and stir for 1–2 minutes, or until the mixture is fragrant and the greens have wilted. Using the back of a spoon, make an indent in the centre of the mixture and crack the egg into it.

3   Partially cover with a lid and cook, untouched, for 3–4 minutes, or until the white of the egg has set and the yolk is still runny. Season well with salt and pepper. Take the pan straight to table and serve with the toasted sourdough alongside.

# Cauliflower scramble

**DF**   **VEG**

**SERVES** 1
**PREP** 15 MINUTES
**COOK** 10 MINUTES

————

1 tablespoon coconut oil
125 g (1 cup) small cauliflower
    florets
2 spring onions, thinly sliced
2 large eggs, whisked
small handful of fresh mixed
    herbs (basil, flat-leaf parsley,
    mint)
1 slice of sourdough, toasted
lemon wedge, to serve

1   Heat the oil in a non-stick frying pan over medium–high heat. Add the cauliflower and cook, stirring occasionally, for 3 minutes or until the cauliflower is starting to soften and turn golden.

2   Add the spring onion and eggs, and use a spatula to scramble everything together. Cook for 2–3 minutes or until the egg is softly set.

3   Remove the pan from the heat, stir through the herbs then serve hot with the toasted sourdough and a lemon wedge alongside.

**Mushrooms and greens with egg**

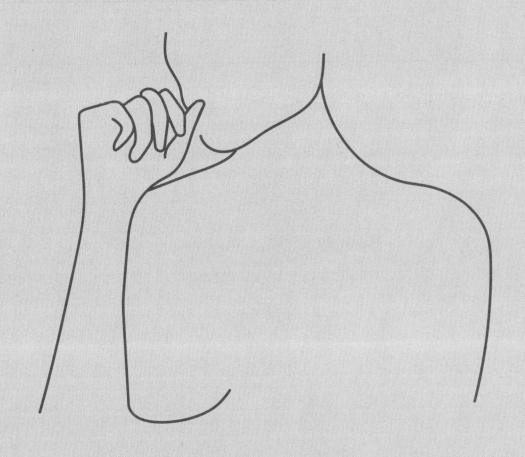

# Make mealtimes a no-phone zone

---

*Being constantly distracted is a fact of life now, but it's not great for our minds and bodies. I make it a point never to eat with my phone near me.*

# We have to disconnect to reconnect

We have to *remove ourselves* from the chaos around us, so we can tune in to our appetites and *reconnect* to our beautiful bodies in a *loving way.*

One morning about a year ago, I made my fluffy protein pancakes topped with extra-creamy Greek yoghurt, cinnamon and berries. For some reason, I broke my 'no social media at mealtimes' rule and found myself scrolling through Instagram. But after a couple of minutes, I found myself back in the kitchen and rummaging through my fridge. I was hungry. But I'd just eaten?

I suddenly realised my mind hadn't registered that I'd eaten breakfast because it had been so consumed with digesting my Instagram feed. It's like my brain had forgotten about the meal and I was completely unsatisfied.

Being distracted is one of the major reasons people overeat; they're simply not paying attention to the food they're eating. Consequently, they don't register their body's cues. Computers and TVs play a role in this distraction epidemic, but without a doubt, the biggest offender is the smartphone – which connects us to social media 24/7.

While social media has a place in the world, that place is not at mealtimes. It takes over our thought processes and distracts us from eating mindfully. In my opinion, our obsessive use of social media is worsening our relationship with food, causing us to feel unsatisfied at mealtimes, which can lead to overeating, emotional eating and fast eating – none of which is good for our digestion or our body image.

## Scrolling adds stress AND messes up our digestion

When we eat, our body needs to focus on breaking down our food. But if we scroll through our feeds while we eat, it dulls the signals to the digestive system, and our brain finds it harder to register whether we're full. Social media causes comparison and anxiety, which are barriers to mindful eating.

Research shows that phone use increases our heart rate, blood pressure and anxiety levels. Arianna Huffington's book *Thrive* explains how, when we get an email or message, our heart races in anticipation as we wonder if the message will contain good news or bad news, or if it will add a task to our (already crazy) to-do list.

*Make mealtimes a no-phone zone*

This has a huge impact not only on digestion, but also on our attitudes to food. Even if we're feeling good about the food we're eating, an email, text or social media post can derail all of that. I bet you can think of a recent moment when this happened to you. Whenever I break my no-phone rule, I regret it for this very reason.

# A healthy life involves setting boundaries with social media

Boundaries are crucial. If you're familiar with my work, you'll know I talk extensively about the importance of tuning in to your body and giving it exactly what it needs. However, it's very hard to register your body's satiety (fullness) signals if you're busy scrolling through various feeds and catching up on the world around you.

We're so connected to everything external via our phones, emails, social media and social lives that we've disconnected from our own beautiful body. We've forgotten how to tune in to its needs and signals.

If you've been struggling with this disconnection, it's not your fault. It's a product of the hyper-connected world we live in.

But for every problem there's a solution. In this chapter, I'm going to guide you through the process of setting boundaries with social media – especially in the mornings and evenings. Doing this gives us the time we need to decompress and re-energise the mind and drastically reduce stress levels. These boundaries have helped me to heal my relationship with food and to find balance in my everyday life. I hope they'll do the same for you.

## Baby steps

First up, I want you to unfollow immediately any social media accounts that make you feel anxious, guilty or like you're not enough. Unfollow people who promote unrealistic ideals and cause you to compare yourself with them. You'll be amazed at how liberating it feels.

Next, I'd like you set social media boundaries that work with your lifestyle. Here are the ones that work for me:

- I delete all social media apps and turn my phone off at 8 pm.
- I don't check social media until I've woken up and completed my calming morning routine (pages 56–57).
- I try not to check social media more than three times a day.
- When I'm resting, I leave my phone in another room so I'm not tempted to scroll.
- I don't use my phone at all when I eat.

These boundaries have lifted my energy levels and brought a sense of peace to my everyday life. Learning the art of mindful eating is also essential if you want to tune in to your body and listen to its cues. If you can follow these guidelines, you'll soon have zero desire to pick up your phone at mealtimes.

# Mindful eating means freedom with food. Finally!

Mindfulness is a practice that can be applied to every aspect of your life. Essentially, mindfulness is being aware of the present moment and avoiding distraction. When we're not thinking of the past or worrying about the future, we're able to live in the here and now. Mindfulness can be a powerful tool to making healthier food and lifestyle choices in our everyday lives.

It's time to slow down and tune in to our bodies.

It's time to ENJOY the plate of food in front of you, not stress about it.

I'm now a mindful eater. Being mindful during meals and feeling connected to the act of eating enables me to connect to food in a positive way. It also helps me to feel more satisfied and nourished at each meal.

To eat mindfully, start by following the tips in my mindful eating toolbox below. These little changes may take some time to get used to, but trust me when I say you'll soon count them among your favourite healthy habits.

## My mindful eating toolbox

Here's how to set yourself up for a mindful meal, and enjoy less stress and better digestion.

1 Before you eat, stash your phone in a different room and ban yourself from using your phone or computer at mealtimes. Like all habits, it just takes practice – the benefits to your mental and physical health are huge.

2 Enjoy a tech detox after mealtimes too, to aid digestion. Give your body 15–20 minutes to digest in peace, without the noise of social media and emails. I understand this isn't realistic at every mealtime, so just do it when you can – like on weekends.

3 Avoid social media first thing in the morning, as this can negatively affect your energy, mood and eating choices for the rest of the day. Instead, try starting your day with a grounding morning routine (pages 56–57).

4 Tune in to your body and appetite, and think about what you feel like eating. When you diet, you usually eat

whatever you're 'meant' to eat. For your next meal, figure out what you're in the mood to eat. What are you craving? Once you work out what you want to eat, add that food to your plate and enjoy every bite. If it's not nutritious, that's okay. Just aim to make your next meal healthy.

5    Stop with the 'all-or-nothing' approach. If you eat imperfectly, forgive yourself, move on, and make a healthier choice at your next meal. Don't write the day off or judge yourself too harshly. Be aware of how you eat, but not to the point of negative judgement. If you're hoping to eat better, make a note to do that at the next meal, then breathe deeply and let it go. Your body can handle it.

6    Plate up your food and sit down to eat it. I only eat once I've put my food on a plate and I'm sitting at the table. Please do the same – it does wonders for your digestion.

7    Make your meals pleasurable and enjoyable. Eating is one of life's simplest pleasures, so I relish mealtimes! I see them as a break from my day, and a time to check in with myself. I set aside 20 minutes to prepare and savour my food. If I have a little time, I love to make my meals look pretty and appetising with herbs, greens, spices or other garnishes. I realise this isn't doable for every meal – but just being more conscious can really help you to heal your relationship with food.

**Top tip:** As always, small steps lead to big changes. If you can't go cold turkey just yet, try putting your phone away for a day's worth of meals. I bet you'll become addicted to the feeling.

# TESTIMONIAL

*'You really can enjoy the foods you love, without the guilt and still reach your weight-loss goals. It's about how you feel, and if you feel good, you look good. It's ok to put yourself first and not feel guilty about it.'*

# Rein in your technology use

I set tech boundaries in other areas of my life, not just around mealtimes. Thanks to these boundaries, I find I'm calmer, less anxious clearer-headed and more focused. I'm more productive and the quality of my work is better.
Here's what works for me.

## Email

- I only check my email three times a day (when possible): first thing in the morning, at lunchtime and again around 3 pm. Once I'm done, I quit the Mail app. I know I can always reopen it if something urgent comes up.
- I attend to all my emails as soon as I start work in the morning. I don't leave emails sitting in my inbox. I address each one, and then file them away. I swear this clears space in my brain!
- I delete emails that don't add value to my life or work. This sounds harsh, but honestly, it gives me the energy to do what I need to do.
- I say NO more often than YES on email. If I know an opportunity isn't something I want to pursue, I say a clear but polite no right away, to eliminate any further back and forth.
- I use the Slack instant-messaging app to chat to my team members. It's an amazing tool for organisation, and it's also lowered the number of emails that fly into my inbox every day.

## Phone

- I leave my phone on silent, off vibrate, all day. This way, I'm not distracted every time it pings. However, if you're a parent or caregiver and want to make sure you can be reached if necessary, leaving your phone on vibrate might be the best you can do.
- I pick up the phone to discuss more complex matters. A quick call can get the job done so much faster while back-and-forth emails can be so exhausting – do you agree?
- When I'm finished checking social media, I completely delete the apps from my phone so I'm not tempted to scroll while I'm working. It's so easy to quickly re-download the apps.
- I also delete the apps from my phone before I go to bed.
- If you don't want to delete the apps, I'd suggest storing them in a folder on your phone that's harder to access.
- I opt out of notifications on my phone. I have to manually check for texts, emails and Instagram comments. The silence is so healing (and freeing!).

# How I transitioned from being a dieter to an intuitive eater

As you now know, in my teens and early twenties I was a chronic fad dieter. I listened to my diet 'rules' and calorie-counting devices – not my body. Definitely not my body.

For years, I blocked my real hunger signals so I could stick to whatever diet I was on. This became a habit, which made it hard for me to tune in to how food made me feel. As a result, I was unable to determine when I was full or hungry. How could I know? Diets disconnected me from my own body, and often led to overeating or poor food choices.

I didn't see food as nourishment, or as fuel that could lift my mood and energy, and help me to thrive. Instead, I judged food purely on its calorie content, and how 'good' it would be for my waistline.

Because I was so disconnected from my body, my relationship with food started to suffer. And this led to fast eating and mindless eating. I inhaled my food in minutes. When you're a fad dieter, you always feel that food is scarce – because diets are all about restriction. Thanks to this fear or not having 'enough' food, you have an urge to eat everything in front of you as soon as you can. And you're physically hungry, so that also makes you want to devour your meals quickly.

I'm here to tell you that your food isn't going anywhere.

> **Remind yourself that you can *always* eat more food later.**

This change in perspective is the best part about transitioning from fad dieter to wholefood, balanced eater. Those feelings of deprivation start to dissolve and, as a result, you begin to relax around food. The need to overeat, binge eat or inhale your food dissipates too.

## My top tips to overcome FAST eating

Slooow down. You can have more food later or tomorrow, so what's the rush? Try these tips:

- Let go of the 'my diet starts tomorrow' mentality. This is a toxic way of thinking that triggers anxiety about the lack of food, which makes you eat faster at mealtimes. Instead, tell yourself 'I eat with balance, every day'. Literally say this out loud until it sinks in.
- Put your food on a plate, and don't eat while standing or doing something else. At mealtimes, give your food your full attention.

THE 12-STEP MIND-BODY-FOOD RESET

- Take three deep breaths before your meal. This immediately calms down your nervous system and encourages you to eat slower. It reduces anxiety around food, and helps the digestive system to do its job. Deep breathing takes practice, so be patient.
- Avoid eating while you're on the go. With our fast-paced lifestyles, this isn't always possible, but aim to eat when you're in a calm and peaceful environment – even if that means waiting a little longer for your food.
- Express gratitude for the plate of food in front of you. You're so lucky to have access to beautiful, nourishing food. Turn any feelings of guilt, anxiety or stress into gratitude – the Pre-Meal Meditation below will help.
- Savour each mouthful of food. Eating is such a pleasurable experience. Enjoy it!
- Stabilise your blood sugar levels by eating three satiating meals and two snacks. That way, you won't arrive at a meal too hungry to control your pace or choices. See Chapter 3 for a refresher about eating with balance.

*Activity*

# MY PRE-MEAL MEDITATION

Before every meal, I say a silent prayer of gratitude for the food in front of me. This mini-meditation has healed my relationship with food and helped me to eat more mindfully. I suggest doing this at least once or twice a week.

1   Sit down and take three long, deep breaths.

2   Switch off any phones, computers and TVs in your eating environment.

3   Look at your food and say, 'Thank you for this plate of goodness.' Gratitude is everything. It calms down the mind and body.

4   Replace negative thoughts or feelings about food, like fear or guilt, with positive affirmations, such as 'My body will feel so nourished after eating this,' or 'My body knows how to turn this food into fuel.'

5   Take small mouthfuls, chew them properly and savour the flavours.

6   After your meal, say, 'Thank you for nourishing my body.'

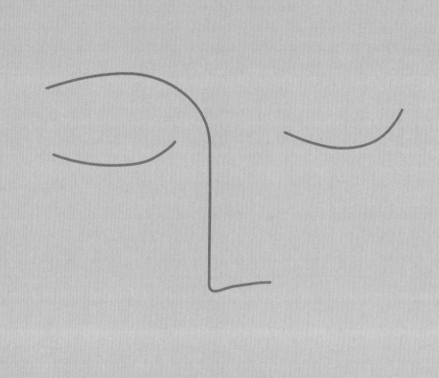

# 6

# Spend an hour prepping for a healthy week

*If you can commit just 1 hour a week to prepping, you'll set yourself up for a week of healthy choices and cooking.*

# Prep for success

Many people feel that they don't have the time to live the healthy life. I get it! Over the last couple of years, I've been building a business, managing a team and juggling projects – and I've often found myself short on time. This has inspired me to find ways to live healthily while saving time and stress.

That brings us here. You've heard the saying 'preparation is the key to success'? Well, when it comes to health and nutrition, this couldn't be truer.

Let me show you how to make prep a part of your weekly routine.

## My step-by-step guide to Sunday prep

To make sure I stay on track with healthy eating, I spend an hour or two food prepping every Sunday or Monday. That way, I have everything I need to whip up a nutritious meal quickly, no matter how busy I get. Try following these steps and prepping a few things this weekend, and I bet you'll feel less overwhelmed during the week (and less inclined to order takeaway).

1   Plan your meals and snacks for the week. By doing this, you'll know exactly what to shop for, and you won't waste time or money. Once you've done that, write a shopping list for those recipes. (I've put my full shopping list on pages 100–101 if you want to use that as a guide.)

2   Go grocery shopping. Hit the farmers' market or supermarket and shop efficiently, following the plan of attack on pages 96–97.

3   Prepare food in bulk. Now it's time to get cooking! You'll find some of my go-to weekly meals to prep from page 102. Below is a list of my favourite foods to make in bulk, and how long they last (in a good airtight container in the fridge).

   – boiled eggs (2–3 days)
   – brown rice and quinoa (2–3 days)
   – grilled meat (2–3 days)
   – roasted veggies (2–3 days)
   – raw veggies: e.g. chopped carrots, cucumber or beetroot (4–5 days)
   – spiralised zucchini (3–4 days)
   – salad mix (washed and dried): e.g. lettuce, rocket, spinach (4–5 days)

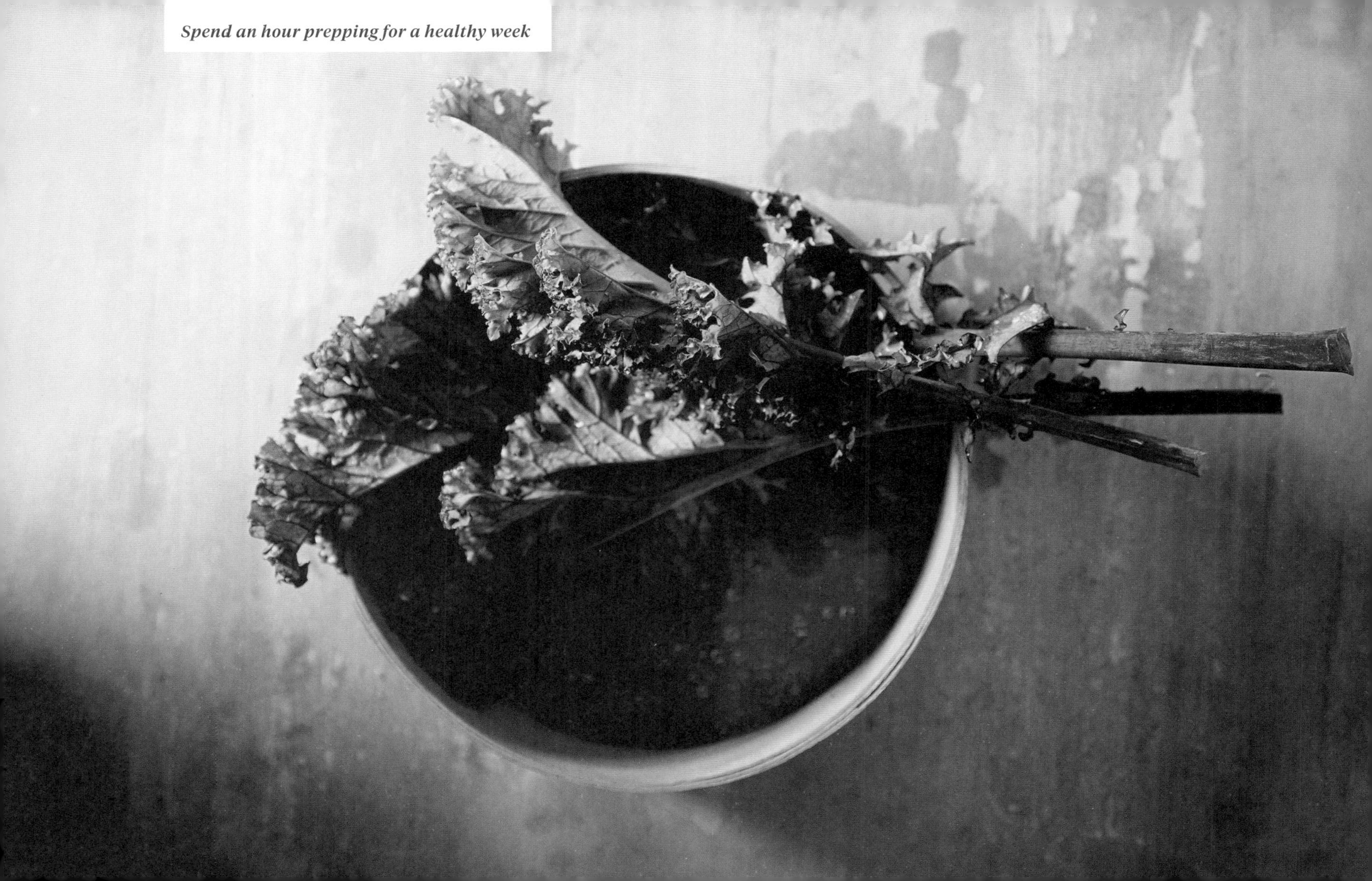

*Spend an hour prepping for a healthy week*

**4** Chop now, eat later. And speaking of veggies, I wash and chop mine as soon as I buy them. Lettuce, carrots, cauliflower florets, broccoli, cucumber, kale ... Anything I've just bought gets prepped when I get home. This takes 10–15 minutes, but it cuts down on prep time during the week, and it makes for super-easy roasting, stir-frying or steaming. It also makes it less likely that they'll end up neglected at the bottom of the fridge.

**5** I pre-rice: if brown rice, quinoa or cauliflower or broccoli 'rice' is on the menu for the week, I also make that on my prep day. It's so easy to make cauliflower or broccoli rice: just pulse the raw veggie in a food processor or finely chop until it reaches the consistency of rice, then store in an airtight container for up to 4 days. I love these rices as bases for a meal, and you can get really creative with the recipes or keep them super simple. Just gently fry the veggie rice for a few minutes, add some protein and a healthy starch (such as sweet potato) and, voilà! You've got a nutritionally balanced meal.

> **Top tip:** Learn to love a mason jar! I store raw nuts, seeds, superfoods, oats, flaxseed and almond meal in mason jars, and keep these in my fridge. That way, they stay extra fresh, and they're ready to go when I am. If your budget won't stretch to mason jars, save glass jars after using them.

# Set your kitchen up to support healthy eating

I arrange my kitchen in a way that works for me, and makes cooking easy and effortless.

## Set up a 'flavour tray' close to your cooking station

Above my stove, I keep a tray of the ingredients I use the most to add flavour to my meals. The tray includes cold-pressed extra-virgin olive oil, coconut oil, tamari, garlic cloves, fresh lemons, sesame seeds, nutritional yeast, and all the fresh herbs and spices I list on page 245. This means I don't have to waste time hunting in the pantry, because everything I need is within easy reach.

**Top tip:** Most health-food stores now sell delicious dried herb mixes that flavour meals so well. Avoid any mixed spices that contain added sugar, salt or preservatives.

## Equip yourself

Have two sturdy roasting trays on hand so you can roast big batches of vegetables (see pages 150–51).

Keep any appliances you'll need for your hourly prep session, such as the blender, food processor and spiraliser, in easy reach and ready to go.

## Clear some space

Not only will you need space to do your prep, you'll also need enough room in your fridge and freezer to store all that healthy food. So before you prep, spend 1–2 minutes making space. There's nothing better after a busy day than remembering you've got a delicious meal waiting for you in the freezer.

## Stock up on storage

If you can, invest in good-quality food-storage containers of varying sizes that are also airtight. If these containers also happen to be dishwasher-, freezer-, oven- AND microwave-safe, even better! You'll be able to take your meal straight from the freezer to the oven, and then to the dishwasher without issue.

## Use it or lose it

Clear out your fridge and pantry regularly to identify any food that has either expired or is close to it. Move anything that needs to be used up to the front of the fridge, so you're reminded to use it every time you open the door.

# Shop in just 15 minutes. I do!

Not only do I not want to spend hours making meals during the week, I also don't want to spend all day at the supermarket – nor do I have to. Fifteen minutes is all I need! Once you get the hang of cooking quick and easy meals, shopping will become easier and quicker. That's because when you keep things simple and have a well-stocked pantry full of healthy staples, you know exactly what you need – and, more importantly, what you don't.

I actually find that health-conscious people buy less! Why is this? As food writer Michael Pollan says, the goal is to shop around the supermarket. When you follow a healthy lifestyle, there's no need to navigate the middle aisles because those shelves are usually filled with processed and packaged foods. When you wander those aisles, you'll be tempted to add all sorts of extras to your basket. On the other hand, if you stick to the outskirts of the supermarket, you'll find fruit, veggies, high-quality meat and dairy. You'll save yourself a ton of time and money (and you won't feel bloated 24/7) – just ask my husband! Our grocery bill has gone down since I started living the healthy life.

> **If I can't pronounce it,** *I don't eat it!*

## What to know before you go

Nutrition labels can be overwhelming (and quite sneaky), but when you're trying to live a healthy, happy life, it's really important to know how to read them so that you understand what you're putting in your body before you put it into your shopping trolley.

I follow one simple rule. A product's ingredients appear in descending order from the main ingredient onwards. That means the first ingredient listed is what makes up most of that product, and so on. For example, if you read a peanut butter label and notice that 'peanuts' is pretty far down the ingredients list, you know that the spread doesn't actually contain many peanuts all. Or, with yoghurt and jam, you may see 'sugar' as the first or second ingredient, which means you'll basically be eating spoonfuls of sugar. No thanks! Here are a few basic things to look out for.

**Nutrition panel:** The top section spells out the serving size. For instance, a yoghurt label may say it contains a percentage of sugar, fat and carbohydrates 'per 100 g', but that particular serving of yoghurt might be 200 g ... So you need to double those numbers to get the actual amount of sugar you'd be consuming per serve. Cheeky, right?

**Fat content:** The most important percentage to look at is the saturated and/or trans fats. Trans fats are mostly found in baked, fried and frozen foods. Avoid foods with margarine, hydrogenated vegetable oil, canola oil and soybean oil, as these are usually highly processed and therefore harder for our bodies to metabolise. Also, 'low-fat' products tend to contain sugar, artificial sweeteners and preservatives to make them taste better, so be careful.

**Sugar content:** Avoid any product that lists sugar as the main ingredient. After that, only eat food with 3 g of sugar or less per serve. Steer clear of foods with high fructose corn syrup – it's a cheap, processed sweetener that's linked to diabetes and obesity.

**Sodium or salt content:** Salt sneaks its way into everything, from breads and cereals to chips, roasted nuts and snack packs. We only need to eat one teaspoon of salt a day. So look for products containing 250 mg–300 mg of salt/sodium per 100 g. If a food has 400 mg or more, put it back on the shelf.

**Monosodium glutamate (MSG):** Typically found in Asian cuisine, canned soups and processed meats, MSG is a flavour enhancer that's generally safe, but some people are sensitive to it. The most common symptoms of MSG sensitivity include headaches, muscle tightness, general weakness, numbness and tingling. I personally feel awful and really thirsty when I eat food flavoured with MSG, so I avoid it.

**Artificial sweeteners (aspartame):** These nasties – along with sugar alcohols such as sorbitol, mannitol and isomalt – are hidden in lots of food products. You want to aim for all-natural ingredients wherever you can.

# TESTIMONIALS

*'During the program I could feel my mindset shifting to a new way of thinking and seeing food. Slowly, along with that, I could feel my body change, my clothes fitting a bit better and I started to get a few comments . . . I ate pizza and pancakes and still lost 7 kilos!'*

*'Over the course of 20 months I have lost 40 kilos without dieting or extremes . . . I have regained my self-confidence and I feel utterly amazing.'*

# Your 15-minute healthy shopping plan

If you're starting a healthy lifestyle from scratch and want to stock up on wholefoods, my full shopping list is on pages 100–101. Once you've got the basics sorted, here's my guide to getting in and out with the weekly essentials, quickly!

## First, skim the aisles to pick up your pantry items.
*5 minutes*

*My* go-to pantry staples are:

- ♥ grains: oats, brown rice and quinoa
- ♥ tinned foods: lentils, beans, tuna and salmon
- ♥ nut butters: almond butter and peanut butter
- ♥ tahini
- ♥ sauces: sugar-free Napoletana sauce and pesto
- ♥ healthy pasta: brown rice pasta, mung bean pasta, pulse pasta and konjac or shiritaki noodles
- ♥ baking products: almond meal, coconut flour and baking powder
- ♥ spices: Himalayan salt and black peppercorns
- ♥ nuts and seeds
- ♥ organic eggs (see my thoughts on organic food on pages 98–99)
- ♥ dijon mustard
- ♥ vinegars: balsamic vinegar and apple cider vinegar
- ♥ healthy oils: cold-pressed extra-virgin olive oil and coconut oil
- ♥ drinks: tea, coffee and filtered water

# Now hit the fresh food section.
*5–7 minutes*

*My* **go-to goodies are:**

- ♥ colourful vegetables and greens (see page 100)
- ♥ avocados
- ♥ fresh herbs
- ♥ fruit: berries, banana, papaya and green apples
- ♥ dairy: Greek yoghurt and organic cow's milk
- ♥ dairy-free: almond milk (no added sugar) and coconut yoghurt
- ♥ cheese: ricotta cheese and mozzarella

**Top tips**

Enjoy a protein-rich snack before you go to the shops. Never arrive at a supermarket hungry – you're more likely to buy unnecessary snacks, and who can blame you?

If I'm really short on time, I'll buy pre-cut veggies or cauliflower rice, broccoli rice and zoodles, plus pre-washed lettuce.

Shop online for delivery every Sunday or Monday! Most supermarkets will deliver groceries to your door for an affordable price. This saves you time, and leads to less browsing and temptation. You're also less likely to forget items.

# On a budget?

Healthy eating can be expensive – but there are plenty of ways to cut costs when doing your weekly shop. It's important to spend within your means, so here are my tips for grocery shopping without breaking your budget.

- Map out your meals for the week, and shop with a list. If you have a plan of attack, you're more likely to stay on track. Otherwise, it's easy to stray and fall victim to clever marketing.
- Go no-frills. For things like Greek yoghurt, nuts, grains, crackers and tinned foods, there's no need to buy the fancy brands. The cheapest options should be just fine.
- If you live in a city, buy nuts, seeds, superfoods and grains in bulk at specialty stores. Now that the world is becoming more health-conscious, these stores are popping up everywhere, and refilling your own containers means less packaging. Bonus!
- Choose the oddly shaped and riper fruits and veggies. These may not be the prettiest, but you're probably going to chop them up anyway! They're often cheaper and still taste delicious.
- When bananas start to go brown, don't throw them away; slice them up then put them in the freezer to use for smoothies or 'nice-cream' (recipes for this on my blog; it's so easy!)
- Buy seasonal produce: fruit and veggies are cheaper when they're more readily available.
- Visit farmers' markets. The stalls are stocked with fresh, seasonal produce at much cheaper prices than the supermarkets – and you'll know exactly where your food is coming from.
- Make bigger batches of meals so you have leftovers. I usually cook extra food at dinner so I have something to eat for lunch the next day. This saves me time and money, and some foods taste even better the next day.
- Turn to tinned proteins. Ingredients like tinned lentils, chickpeas, beans or tuna are cheap, and perfect for when you're in a pinch.
- Stick to the basics. Oats, brown rice, eggs and minced meat are inexpensive and versatile.
- Cut back on alcohol. If you're embracing a healthier life, you might already be drinking less. Booze is expensive, and it's easy to spend a significant amount of money on it on a weekly basis. I go alcohol-free during the week.

## Do I only buy organic?

I'm not the nutritionist who's going to tell you to only buy organic food. From a budget point of view, this is just not realistic for most people. I'd rather you focus on getting in all your food groups.

Personally, I aim to eat organic products where possible, especially when it comes to meat, and certain fruits and veggies. Organic foods decrease your exposure to pesticides and can increase your nutrient intake. Foods with thick skins (like bananas and avocados) tend to be safer than those with thinner skins (like grapes or lettuce).

But if you are going to spend money on any organic food, start with the 'dirty dozen'. These are the foods that are most affected by pesticides, as their skins are thinner. In addition to the dirty dozen listed below, I usually opt for organic versions of broccolini, cauliflower, brussels sprouts, zucchini and tomatoes.

# This guide will help you to allocate your pennies

| 'Dirty dozen' (the most sprayed) | Cleanest of the bunch |
|---|---|
| X Apples | ✓ Asparagus |
| X Celery | ✓ Sweet corn |
| X Strawberries | ✓ Peas |
| X Peaches | ✓ Avocado |
| X Spinach | ✓ Papaya |
| X Nectarines | ✓ Broccoli |
| X Grapes | ✓ Cauliflower |
| X Capsicums | ✓ Bananas |
| X Potatoes | ✓ Mangoes |
| X Lettuce | ✓ Onions |
| X Blueberries | ✓ Kiwifruit |
| X Kale | ✓ Pineapples |

**Top tip:** Missed the farmers' markets? To wash off residual pesticides and herbicides from conventional produce, place your fruits and veggies in water with a couple of tablespoons of apple cider vinegar. Let them soak for 10 minutes before rinsing and then store in the fridge.

# My fridge and pantry essentials

When it comes to grocery shopping, it's really important that I spend money on food that supports my health and reflects my values. Unless otherwise specified in my recipes, I use ingredients that are organic, seasonal and free-range whenever I can (see pages 98–99 for my organic food basics).

## Veggies

- [ ] Broccoli
- [ ] Brussels sprouts
- [ ] Carrots
- [ ] Cauliflower
- [ ] Celery
- [ ] Cucumber
- [ ] Greens: lettuce, kale, spinach and rocket
- [ ] Leek
- [ ] Spring onion
- [ ] Onion
- [ ] Pumpkin
- [ ] Sweet potato
- [ ] Tomatoes
- [ ] Zucchini
- [ ] Eggplant

## Fruits

- [ ] Green apples
- [ ] Avocados
- [ ] Bananas
- [ ] Berries, fresh and frozen
- [ ] Lemons
- [ ] Limes
- [ ] Oranges
- [ ] Papaya
- [ ] Pomegranate
- [ ] Medjool dates, fresh

**Fresh Medjool dates have less sugar than dried!**

## Fresh herbs and spices

- [ ] Chilli flakes
- [ ] Ground cinnamon
- [ ] Ground cumin
- [ ] Curry powder
- [ ] Moroccan spice mix
- [ ] Fresh herbs: parsley, basil, mint and coriander
- [ ] Garlic
- [ ] Ginger
- [ ] Paprika (sweet)
- [ ] Pepper
- [ ] Salt: Himalayan or sea salt
- [ ] Turmeric

## Protein

Preferably organic, free-range and pasture-raised
- [ ] Beef: grass-fed
- [ ] Chicken, cage-free
- [ ] Eggs, cage-free
- [ ] Lamb
- [ ] Turkey
- [ ] Fish, tinned or fresh: white fish and wild salmon
- [ ] Legumes: chickpeas, black beans and lentils
- [ ] Whey, rice or pea protein powder

**Source MSC-certified!**

## Protein powders

I recommend: Nuzest Clean Lean Protein (vegan pea protein) and MyProtein Impact Whey Protein (sweetened with stevia).

**Free from gluten, GMOs, artificial sweeteners, colours and preservatives**

## Nuts and seeds

- ☐ Raw almonds
- ☐ Sesame seeds
- ☐ Raw cashews
- ☐ LSA mix
- ☐ Sunflower seeds
- ☐ Pepitas

## Dairy and dairy alternatives

- ☐ Ricotta, mozzarella, parmesan – these are my personal faves!
- ☐ Organic butter
- ☐ Yoghurt: natural, Greek-style and coconut yoghurt with no added sugar
- ☐ Almond milk or coconut milk

## Gluten-free flours and baking ingredients

- ☐ Almond meal
- ☐ Coconut flour
- ☐ Rolled oats or wheat-free oats
- ☐ Baking powder – aluminium- and gluten-free

## Gluten-free grains and pasta

- ☐ Rice: brown, basmati or wild
- ☐ Quinoa: any colour
- ☐ Pasta alternatives: black bean, brown rice, edamame or mung bean
- ☐ Konjac noodles

**I try to use cacao instead of cocoa in baking**

## Cooking essentials

- ☐ Apple cider vinegar
- ☐ Balsamic vinegar
- ☐ Cold-pressed extra-virgin olive oil, for salads or low–medium heat cooking
- ☐ Virgin coconut oil, for high heat cooking
- ☐ Sweeteners: pure maple syrup, raw honey and stevia
- ☐ Miso paste
- ☐ Lemon juice

## Condiments and spreads

- ☐ Dijon mustard
- ☐ Tahini (unhulled) and hummus
- ☐ Nut butters: almond butter and peanut butter
- ☐ Napoletana sauce with no added sugar
- ☐ Tamari (gluten-free soy sauce)

## Beverages

- ☐ Caffeinated drinks: coffee, chai, green and black tea
- ☐ Non-caffeinated herbal tea: chamomile, ginger, rooibos chai and peppermint
- ☐ Coconut water
- ☐ Spring and alkaline water

## Superfoods (optional)

- ☐ Acai berry, powder or frozen
- ☐ Raw cacao powder
- ☐ Chia seeds: black or white
- ☐ Coconut, desiccated or shredded
- ☐ Psyllium husk
- ☐ Spirulina

# Vanilla chia oat bircher

**VEG**

**SERVES** 1 (SEE TIP ON
OPPOSITE PAGE)
**PREP** 5 MINUTES
+ OVERNIGHT CHILLING

———

50 g (½ cup) rolled oats
1 tablespoon chia seeds
½ teaspoon vanilla bean powder
180 ml (¾ cup) milk of choice
     (pages 110–11)
40 g (¼ cup) whole natural
     almonds, chopped
1 tablespoon goji berries

1   Place the oats, chia seeds, vanilla and milk in a bowl and stir until well combined. Cover and refrigerate overnight until the mixture is thick and smooth.

2   Add the almonds and goji berries and stir until well combined. Serve topped with one of the options below.

## Make it dairy-free and vegan ...

By using one of my homemade milks on pages 110–11.

## Topping options

**1 RASPBERRY COCONUT**

Lightly crush 60 g (½ cup) of fresh raspberries with a fork then gently swirl those through 2 heaped tablespoons of coconut yoghurt. Spoon this mixture over the bircher then serve sprinkled with a few good pinches of flaked coconut.

**2 APPLE PIE**

Coarsely grate a small green apple into a bowl. Add 2 teaspoons of fresh lemon juice, ½ teaspoon of ground cinnamon and a pitted and chopped medjool date to the apple and stir to combine. Spoon this mixture over the bircher and serve sprinkled with ground cinnamon and 1 tablespoon of pepitas.

**3 TROPICAL BANANA**

Combine ½ a mashed banana with 2 tablespoons of Greek yoghurt and the seeds and juice of a passionfruit. Spoon this mixture over the bircher and serve topped with extra sliced banana and a few small fresh mint leaves, if desired.

**Raspberry coconut**

**Apple pie**

**Tropical banana**

## Prepping for a busy week

Measure single portions of the dry ingredients into mason jars, pop the lid on and store them in your pantry. Simply add milk the night before you want to eat one, stir, and place in the fridge before you go to bed.

# Oatey banana bread breakfast wheels

**VEG**

**MAKES** 12
**PREP** 20 MINUTES
**COOK** 20 MINUTES

---

4 small over-ripe bananas (about
    340 g in total), peeled
3 large eggs, whisked
2 tablespoons pure maple syrup
60 ml (¼ cup) milk of choice
    (pages 110–11)
145 g (1½ cups) rolled oats
35 g (¼ cup) golden flaxmeal
2 tablespoons psyllium husk
1 teaspoon baking powder
2 teaspoons vanilla bean powder
1 teaspoon ground cinnamon
8 large fresh medjool dates,
    pitted and finely chopped
30 g (¼ cup) walnuts, finely
    chopped

1   Preheat the oven to 180°C (160°C fan-forced). Line two large baking trays with non-stick baking paper.

2   Place the bananas in a large bowl and use a fork to mash them really well until smooth. Add the eggs, maple syrup and milk, and whisk together using the fork until everything is well combined. Add the remaining ingredients and stir again until well combined. Let the mixture stand for 3 minutes, or until it thickens slightly.

3   Using a ¼-cup measure, drop level portions of the banana mixture onto the prepared trays, leaving a 3 cm gap between each portion. Flatten each portion slightly into a 7 cm round.

4   Place both trays in the oven at the same time and bake for 18–20 minutes, swapping trays halfway through the cooking time, until the cookies are baked and golden. Leave the wheels to cool on their trays for 3 minutes, then serve warm or let them cool completely on wire racks before storing in an airtight container in the fridge for up to 4 days.

## Here's a serving idea that's messy, but fun and super yum!

Sandwich together TWO of the wheels with a dollop of thick Greek yoghurt and a little drizzle of pure maple syrup, then serve.

# Creamy cannellini, cauliflower and almond soup

**GF**    **DF**    **VEG**    **VEGAN**

**SERVES** 4
**PREP** 15 MINUTES
**COOK** 30 MINUTES

———

2 tablespoons cold-pressed
    extra-virgin olive oil
1 leek, white and light green
    parts only, finely sliced and
    washed
2 garlic cloves, crushed
80 g (½ cup) whole natural
    almonds
1 small cauliflower (about
    600 g), leaves, stems
    and florets chopped
1 teaspoon mixed dried herbs
1.5 litres (6 cups) vegetable
    stock
1 x 400 g tin cannellini beans,
    drained and rinsed well
sea salt and freshly ground
    black pepper
Pistachio dukkah kale chips
    (page 190), to serve

1   Heat the oil in a large saucepan over medium heat. Add the leek and cook, stirring occasionally, for 3 minutes or until it starts to soften.

2   Add the garlic, almonds, cauliflower, herbs and stock, and stir gently until the mixture comes to a simmer. Reduce the heat to medium–low and simmer gently, stirring occasionally, for 20 minutes.

3   Stir in the beans and simmer for a further 5 minutes, or until the beans are heated through.

4   Remove the pan from the heat and allow to cool for 5 minutes. Season well with salt and pepper and then, using a hand-held stick blender, purée the soup until it is completely smooth and creamy. Divide between serving bowls and top with a handful of the pistachio dukkah kale chips.

# Vegan eggplant and chickpea curry

**GF    DF    VEG    VEGAN**

**SERVES** 4
**PREP** 15 MINUTES
**COOK** 35 MINUTES

———

2 tablespoons coconut oil
1 red onion, cut into thin wedges
1 eggplant (about 520 g), cut
    into 3 cm cubes
1 tablespoon curry powder
1 x 400 g tin chickpeas, drained
    and rinsed well
1 x 400 g tin chopped tomatoes
2 large kale leaves, leaves torn,
    thick stems discarded
small handful of coriander sprigs
cooked brown basmati rice,
    quinoa or Garlic vegetable
    fried 'rice' (page 114),
    to serve
toasted slivered almonds,
    to serve

1   Heat the oil in a large, deep non-stick frying pan over high heat. Add the onion and eggplant and cook, stirring occasionally, for 5 minutes, or until the onion has softened and the eggplant is golden.

2   Reduce the heat to medium-low and add the curry powder. Cook and stir for 30 seconds or until the mixture starts to smell fragrant. Add the chickpeas, tomatoes and 250 ml (1 cup) of water, and stir gently until the mixture comes to a simmer. Reduce the heat to low and simmer gently for 25–30 minutes, or until the curry has reduced and thickened.

3   Remove the mixture from the pan and remove the pan from heat. Add the kale to the pan and stir until it wilts down. Serve the curry on a bed of kale then top the curry with the coriander and toasted almonds and some basmati or quinoa alongside. This is also delicious served with garlic vegetable fried 'rice'.

# Three homemade nut milks

**GF    DF    VEG    VEGAN**

## Almond, coconut and vanilla milk

**MAKES** 1 LITRE
**PREP** 30 MINUTES +
OVERNIGHT SOAKING

———

160 g (1 cup) whole natural
   almonds
45 g (½ cup) desiccated coconut
good pinch of sea salt
1 teaspoon vanilla bean powder
1 litre (4 cups) filtered water

1   Put the almonds in a bowl and cover with at least 6 cm of water. Cover the bowl and leave at room temperature overnight (or for at least 12 hours) to soak. Drain well and rinse under cold running water, then drain well again.

2   Place the almonds, coconut, salt and vanilla bean powder in an upright blender and blend until the almonds are finely chopped. Add the filtered water and blend for 2 minutes on high speed until the mixture is completely smooth.

3   Strain the almond milk through a sieve lined with a piece of muslin and set the sieve over a large jug or wide-mouthed jar (you could also use a nut milk bag for this, if you have one). Squeeze the muslin well to ensure you extract as much milk as possible from the nut meal (and see my note below before you throw away that nut meal!).

4   Cover the jug or seal the jar with an airtight lid and keep in the fridge for up to 5 days.

## Macadamia and nutmeg

**MAKES** 1 LITRE
**PREP** 30 MINUTES +
OVERNIGHT SOAKING

—

Follow the same instructions as opposite, with these easy tweaks. Replace almonds with the same quantity of macadamia nuts. Omit the desiccated coconut. Use ½ teaspoon finely grated nutmeg or ¼ teaspoon ground nutmeg in place of the vanilla.

## Hazelnut and cinnamon

**MAKES** 1 LITRE
**PREP** 30 MINUTES +
OVERNIGHT SOAKING

—

Follow the same instructions as opposite, with these easy tweaks. Replace almonds with the same quantity of hazelnuts. Omit the desiccated coconut. Use ½ teaspoon ground cinnamon in place of the vanilla.

### Note

You can keep any leftover nut meals to use in your baking; they are perfect in place of any nutmeals required for brownies or cakes. Just store in an airtight container in the fridge and use within 3 days, or freeze, if you like.

Curried sweet
potato

Cauliflower and
butter bean mash

# Two ways with mash

## Cauliflower and butter bean mash

**GF     DF     VEG   VEGAN**

**SERVES** 4–6
**PREP** 10 MINUTES
**COOK** 15 MINUTES
+ COOLING TIME

———

1 tablespoon cold-pressed
    extra-virgin olive oil
1 small onion, finely chopped
1 garlic clove, crushed
250 g (2 cups) small cauliflower
    florets
1 x 400 g tin butter beans,
    drained and rinsed well
sea salt and freshly ground
    black pepper
½ handful of flat-leaf parsley
    leaves, finely chopped

1 Place the oil, onion, garlic, cauliflower and butter beans in a medium saucepan over medium heat and pour in 125 ml (½ cup) of water.

2 Bring the mixture to a simmer, stirring occasionally, then partially cover with a lid and cook for 10 minutes, stirring occasionally, or until the cauliflower florets are just tender. Remove the pan from the heat and stand, covered, for 5 minutes, then allow to cool to room temperature.

3 Transfer the cauliflower mixture to an upright blender and season well with salt and pepper. Blend until completely smooth, then add 1–2 tablespoons of water if necessary, but no more than that. Stir through the parsley then store in an airtight container in the fridge and use within 2 days.

## Curried sweet potato

**GF     DF     VEG   VEGAN**

**SERVES** 4–6
**PREP** 10 MINUTES
**COOK** 15 MINUTES
+ COOLING TIME

———

1 tablespoon cold-pressed
    extra-virgin olive oil
1 large onion, finely chopped
1 garlic clove, crushed
2 teaspoons curry powder
700 g orange sweet potato,
    peeled and diced
sea salt and freshly ground
    black pepper
½ handful of coriander leaves,
    finely chopped

1 Place the oil, onion, garlic, curry powder and sweet potato in a medium saucepan over medium heat and pour in 125 ml (½ cup) of water.

2 Bring the mixture to a simmer, stirring occasionally, then partially cover with a lid and cook for 10–12 minutes, stirring occasionally, or until the sweet potato is just tender.

3 Remove the pan from the heat and stand, covered, for 5 minutes, then allow to cool to room temperature.

4 Transfer the sweet potato mixture to an upright blender and season well with salt and pepper. Blend until completely smooth then add 1–2 tablespoons of water if necessary, but no more than that. Stir through the coriander leaves then store in an airtight container in the fridge and use within 2 days.

# Garlic vegetable fried 'rice'

**GF  DF  VEG  VEGAN**

**SERVES** 4
**PREP** 20 MINUTES
**COOK** 5 MINUTES

2 zucchini, roughly chopped
250 g (2 cups) small cauliflower
    florets
2 carrots, roughly chopped
2 tablespoons coconut oil
2 garlic cloves, crushed
2 tablespoons chopped chives
sea salt and freshly ground
    black pepper

1   Chop each vegetable separately in a food processor until it starts to resemble rice grains then tip into a large bowl.

2   Heat the oil in a large wok or frying pan over high heat. Add the garlic and stir-fry for 10 seconds, making sure not to let it burn. Add the vegetable rice and stir-fry for 2–3 minutes, or until the rice is just tender. Keep everything moving around the wok.

3   Remove the wok from the heat and toss through the chopped chives. Season well with salt and pepper then store in an airtight container in the fridge for up to 4 days.

## Note

This recipe is an easy, no-fuss mid-week meal. Add the Chinese Fried Rice topping option below to make it a complete meal.

## Flavour options

**1 CURRY FRIED RICE**

Add 1 teaspoon curry powder to the work or frying pan when cooking the garlic, and top with some fresh coriander before serving.

**2 JAPANESE FLAIR**

Grate a 2 cm piece of ginger into the wok with the garlic when cooking. Then add 1 tablespoon each of tamari (gluten-free soy sauce) and toasted sesame seeds when you toss through the chives.

**3 CHINESE FRIED RICE**

Scramble 2 large whisked eggs in the oil before adding the garlic. Then add 1 tablespoon tamari and a generous sprinkle of toasted sesame seeds when you toss through the chives.

# Salmon and sweet potato patties

**G F**   **D F**

**SERVES** 4
**PREP** 20 MINUTES
+ 20 MINUTES CHILL
COOK 15 MINUTES

_____

250 g (1 cup) mashed sweet
    potato (see note)
1 salmon fillet (200 g), skin
    and bones removed, finely
    chopped
1 large egg, whisked
2 tablespoons psyllium husk
2 tablespoons finely chopped
    chives
sea salt and freshly ground
    black pepper
100 g (1 cup) almond meal,
    to coat
coconut oil, to cook
lemon wedges, to serve

1   Place the mashed sweet potato, salmon, egg, psyllium husk and chives in a bowl and season well with salt and pepper, then mix with clean hands until well combined. Cover the bowl and refrigerate for 20 minutes, or until the mixture firms up slightly.

2   Shape the mixture into four even patties about 7 cm round, then put the almond meal on a large plate and coat each patty lightly and evenly on all sides in the almond meal.

3   Heat the coconut oil in a large, non-stick frying pan over medium–low heat. Cook the patties for 12–15 minutes, carefully turning them over halfway through, until cooked through and golden. Keep in an airtight container in the fridge for up to 3 days and serve with lemon wedges.

## Note

You will need 300 g of peeled sweet potato to make 1 cup of mash. Roughly chop the peeled sweet potato, then steam over a saucepan of boiling water for 15–18 minutes, or until a knife passes easily through the largest chunk. Allow it to cool completely before mashing with a fork and using for this recipe.

## Serving options

**1** BREAKFAST
Serve hot with poached eggs and wilted kale leaves.

**2** LUNCH
Serve warm or cooled with a dressed garden salad.

**3** DINNER
Serve hot with steamed greens or between large lettuce leaves with some sliced tomato for a bunless burger.

# Mini cauliflower pizza bases

**GF**  **DF**  **VEG**

**MAKES** 4
**PREP** 20 MINUTES
**COOK** 20 MINUTES

———

250 g (2 cups) small cauliflower
     florets
90 g (½ cup) linseeds
1 large egg, whisked
1 teaspoon dried mixed herbs
45 g (⅓ cup) grated mozzarella
sea salt and freshly ground
     black pepper

1   Preheat the oven to 200°C (180°C fan-forced). Line two large baking trays with non-stick baking paper.

2   Blend all the ingredients in a food processor until the dough is smooth, then season well with salt and pepper. Divide the mixture into four portions then transfer two portions to each of your prepared trays, shaping each portion into a 5 mm-thick round.

3   Bake for 18–20 minutes, swapping the trays halfway through the cooking time. When the bases are cooked and lightly golden, remove from the oven and allow to cool completely on the trays.

4   Transfer the cooled bases to a plate and stack them, placing sheets of non-stick baking paper between them so they don't stick together. Wrap well, then store in the fridge for up to 4 days or in the freezer for up to 2 months.

## When ready to serve ...

Place the pizza bases on separate plates and defrost overnight in the fridge before using.

Top with your favourite pizza toppings then place on baking trays lined with non-stick baking paper and cook in a preheated oven (220°C/200°C fan-forced) for 12–15 minutes to heat your toppings through and allow the base to crisp up.

# Dressings

GF   DF   VEG   VEGAN

## Four-step lemon and herb dressing

**MAKES** ENOUGH FOR
2 LARGE SALADS
**PREP** 15 MINUTES

**STEP 1**
Start with your base: Finely grate the zest of 2 large lemons into a screw-top jar then squeeze their juice into the jar too. Add 60 ml (¼ cup) of cold-pressed extra-virgin olive oil or avocado oil to the jar.

**STEP 2**
Add your seasonings: Add 1 small crushed garlic clove to the jar along with 1 teaspoon of your favourite mustard (dijon or wholegrain), ¼ teaspoon freshly ground black pepper and ½ teaspoon sea salt (or more, to taste).

**STEP 3**
Add fresh herbs: Now add 2 tablespoons of finely chopped herbs of your choice (chives, flat-leaf parsley, basil, rosemary). You can use one herb, or a mixture of your favourites.

**STEP 4**
Shake it up: Firmly secure the lid and shake the jar vigorously for 1 minute, or until well combined and emulsified. Use straight away or keep in the fridge for up to 3 days.

## Teriyaki dressing

**MAKES** ⅓ CUP
**PREP TIME** 5 MINUTES

¼ cup (60 ml) tamari
2 teaspoons sesame oil
2 teaspoons stevia powder or
    raw honey
1 teaspoon grated fresh ginger
1 tablespoon dijon mustard
sea salt and freshly ground
    black pepper

1   Add all of the ingredients to a small bowl and whisk everything together until well combined.

2   Taste and adjust seasoning if necessary and serve with your favourite protein.

## Moroccan tahini dressing

**MAKES** ENOUGH FOR
2 LARGE SALADS
**PREP** 10 MINUTES

———

zest and juice of 2 lemons
1 tablespoon tahini
2 tablespoons cold-pressed
    extra-virgin olive oil
1 small garlic clove, crushed
1 teaspoon ground cumin
1 teaspoon sweet paprika
1 teaspoon ground coriander
½ teaspoon ground turmeric
large pinch dried chilli flakes
1 tablespoon finely chopped
    flat-leaf parsley
2–3 tablespoons warm water
pinch of sea salt and freshly
    ground black pepper

1   Add all the ingredients to a large jug and use a fork
    to whisk everything together until well combined and
    smooth. Add more warm water to loosen, if necessary.

2   Taste and adjust seasoning if necessary, then use right
    away or cover and store in the fridge for up to 3 days.
    Return to room temperature before using and add
    a splash more warm water if needed to loosen again
    after chilling.

# Vegetarian eggplant parmigiana bake

**GF**   **VEG**

**SERVES** 4
**PREP** 10 MINUTES
**COOK** 1 HOUR
+ 10 MINUTES

———

2 large eggplants (about
    1.25 kg), halved lengthways,
    cut sides scored
1 tablespoon cold-pressed
    extra-virgin olive oil
sea salt and freshly ground
    black pepper
large handful of basil leaves
1 x 400 g tin black or brown
    lentils, drained and rinsed
    well
723 g jar sugar-free Napoletana
    sauce
200 g fresh ricotta

1   Preheat the oven to 200°C (180°C fan-forced).

2   Place the eggplant, cut sides facing up, in a large baking
    dish so that they are sitting flat, side by side. Drizzle
    the tops with half the oil and season well with salt and
    pepper. Bake for 40–45 minutes, or until softened and
    golden.

3   Sprinkle three-quarters of the basil leaves over the
    cooked eggplant, then top with the lentils and sauce.

4   Crumble the ricotta evenly over the top, then season
    well with salt and pepper and drizzle with the remaining
    oil. Place the dish back in the oven and bake for 20–25
    minutes, or until the parmigiana is bubbling and golden.
    This is a great one to make and enjoy leftovers from, so
    either serve sprinkled with the remaining basil, or allow
    to cool completely before storing in the fridge. You can
    either reheat portions throughout the week, as needed,
    or reheat the whole batch in the oven for a meal to
    share. This will keep for up to 3 days (see note).

## Note

This recipe also freezes really well for up to 2 months. Just cool
completely before storing each portion in separate airtight containers.

## Make it vegan!

Replace the ricotta with the same amount of
Cauliflower and butterbean mash (page 113) and
leave out the lentils now that you've got those
butterbeans in the mix.

# Vegan lentil bolognese

**GF    DF    VEG  VEGAN**

**SERVES** 4
**PREP** 10 MINUTES
**COOK** 50 MINUTES

——

2 tablespoons cold-pressed
    extra-virgin olive oil
1 onion, finely chopped
1 carrot, finely chopped
2 celery stalks, finely chopped
723 g jar sugar-free Napoletana
    sauce
1 x 400 g tin brown lentils,
    drained and rinsed well
small handful of basil leaves

1   Heat the oil in a large, deep non-stick frying pan over medium–low heat. Add the onion, carrot and celery, and cook, stirring occasionally, for 20 minutes or until the vegetables are very soft.

2   Add the sauce, lentils, basil and 250 ml (1 cup) water, and stir until the mixture comes to a simmer. Continue to cook, stirring occasionally, for 30 minutes, or until the mixture has reduced into a nice rich sauce.

3   Serve right away (see the suggestion below) or store for the week ahead. Allow the bolognese to cool before portioning in airtight containers. This will keep in the fridge for up to 4 days, or in the freezer for up to 3 months.

## Reheat and try one of these easy serving ideas

1   Add 2 teaspoons of sweet paprika and ½ teaspoon of dried chilli flakes to the batch of bolognese while reheating, then spoon it on top of roasted and halved sweet potatoes. Serve with diced avocado and coriander leaves scattered on top.

2   For a non-vegan option, spoon into large grilled field mushrooms then sprinkle with a little goat's feta.

3   Toss through zoodles, brown rice pasta or pulse pasta and top with a few fresh basil leaves (see photo opposite).

4   For a non-vegan option, spread the batch of hot bolognese evenly around into a large, deep frying pan. Make 4 indents in the sauce and crack an egg into each one before cooking over medium heat until the eggs have just set. Serve with lemon wedges.

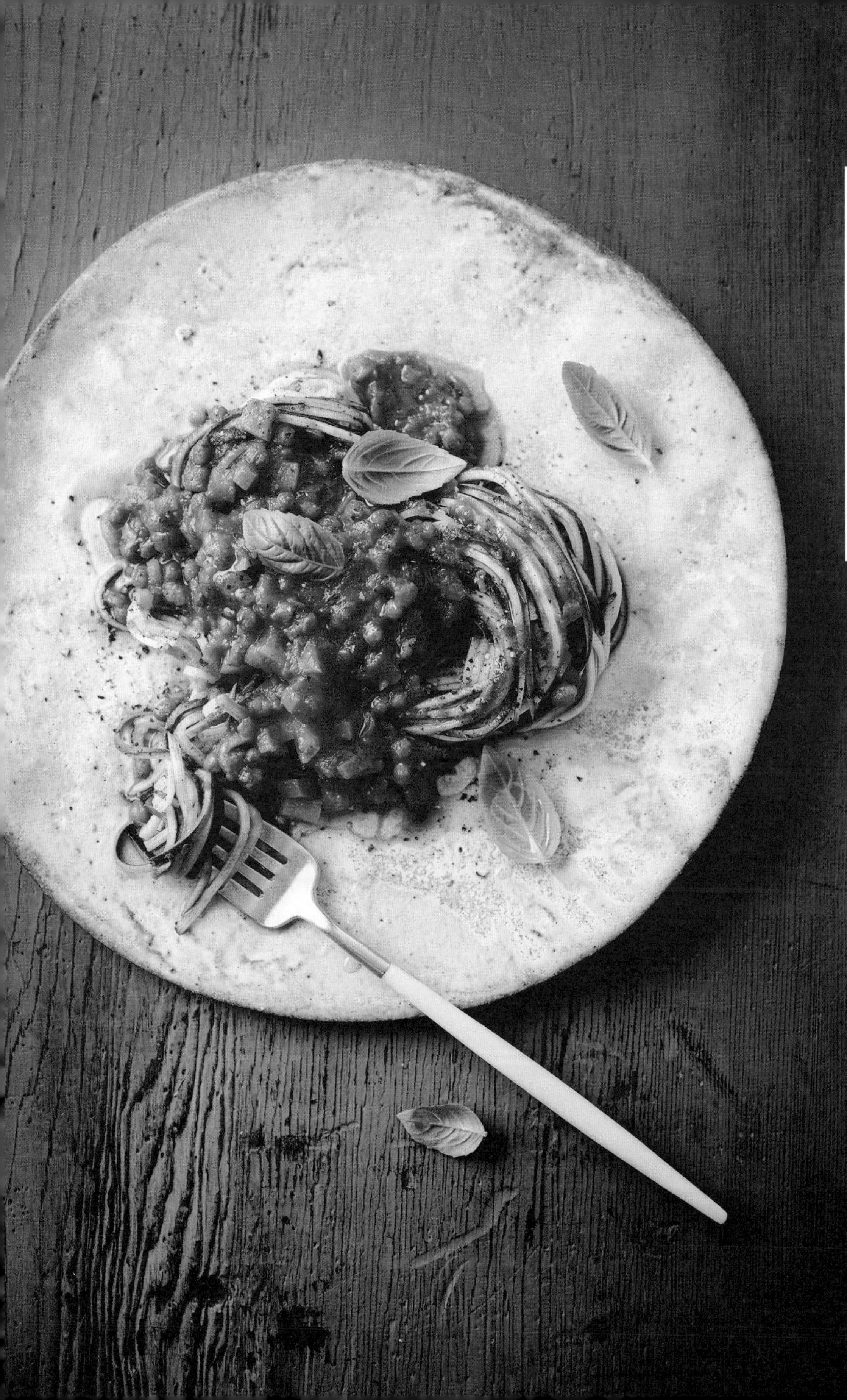

# Cauliflower and seed bread

**GF**  **DF**  **VEG**

**MAKES** 1 LOAF
(SERVES 10–12)
**PREP** 20 MINUTES
**COOK** 1 HOUR

———

2 cups cauliflower rice (see notes)
100 g (1 cup) almond meal
2 tablespoons psyllium husk
2 tablespoons chia seeds
40 g (¼ cup) pepitas, plus 40 g (¼ cup) extra for decorating
1 tablespoon finely chopped rosemary
1 teaspoon sea salt
1 teaspoon curry powder
2 teaspoons baking powder
2 large eggs, whisked
2 tablespoons cold-pressed extra-virgin olive oil

1  Preheat the oven to 160°C (140°C fan-forced). Line the base and sides of a 20 x 10 cm loaf tin with non-stick baking paper.

2  Place all of the ingredients in a large bowl and mix until well combined and smooth. Transfer the dough to the prepared loaf tin, spreading it out evenly and pressing down firmly to level the surface.

3  Sprinkle the top with the extra pepitas then bake for 55–60 minutes, or until the top is golden and a skewer inserted in the centre of the loaf comes out clean. Allow to cool completely in the tin, then turn out and slice to serve. This will keep in an airtight container in the fridge for up to 4 days. To freeze, wrap the slices individually and keep in the freezer for up to 2 months.

## Notes

You can purchase bags or packets of cauliflower rice from your supermarket; just be sure to place it in a clean tea towel and wring out the excess moisture from the grains before using in this loaf.

If you want to make your own, you'll need 1 cauliflower head to get 2 cups of 'rice'. Simply break the head of cauliflower into florets, place these in a food processor and pulse until the cauliflower resembles fine rice-like grains.

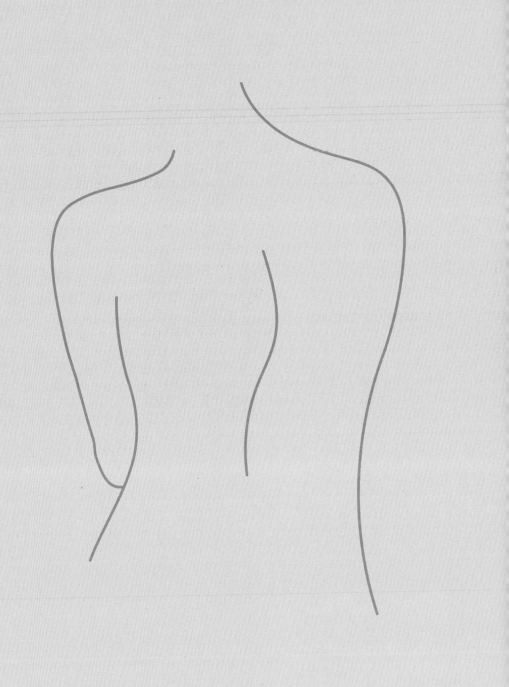

# Manage your stress so it doesn't manage you

---

*We're living with silent stress, so I make time to rest every day – and I don't feel guilty about it.*

# Managing stress changes everything

If we can manage our stress, everything gets easier. Our health gets better, and so does our relationship with our bodies. Life becomes more enjoyable. Some stress is inevitable, but we need to find ways of coping with and reducing our stress so it doesn't build up and create a domino effect in our lives.

The problem is we live in a world where high stress levels are the new normal. Stress streams in from so many different angles, we don't always realise it's there. I call this 'silent stress'.

I believe that social media alone adds a huge amount of stress and anxiety to our lives, and makes it so much harder to accept and love ourselves, and our bodies. The next time you check your phone, tune in to how your body responds. Is your heart racing? Is there a pit in your stomach? Are you clenching your teeth? We chatted about this in Chapter 5, but these responses are examples of the real physical impact of stress.

And I can keep going, because stress affects just about everything, including:

- gut health
- skin
- hormones
- energy levels
- body image
- sleep
- your thyroid gland
- your relationship with food
- your relationships with people
- motivation
- weight.

These are some of the most prevalent issues we are dealing with, yet many of us aren't prioritising stress relief and reduction. We feel guilty about resting and decompressing. There's so much to do and too many hats to wear – how can we possibly stop to rest?

I still feel guilty when I take time off, but I'm working on this. Because I know that when I don't take the time to rest and reset, my mental and physical health starts to suffer. And when it comes down to it, our health is all we have.

# Cortisol (aka the 'stress hormone')

We touched on cortisol earlier in this book, but I want to delve a little deeper. The human body has an incredibly delicate relationship with cortisol; we need it to wake up feeling energised and motivated, but when our cortisol levels are thrown out of whack, our sleep, other hormones, weight and energy can all suffer. And, if our cortisol levels stay too high for too long, we can fall into a state known as 'adrenal fatigue'. At this point, your exhausted body sends the cortisol levels crashing down, making it hard to muster the motivation to do anything. Sometimes, you may feel you have zero energy to lift your head off the pillow, let alone get out of bed and do what you need to do in your day.

In a nutshell, we need cortisol to tackle our days – but many of us have too much cortisol coursing through our bodies. The balance is off, and this means our bodies are in a constant state of stress.

We all know how frazzled and defeated we feel when we're stressed. I'm all about solutions though, so in this chapter I'm going to suggest some methods to help us all better control and manage our stress.

The strategies I'm sharing with you have helped me immensely. I'm a wife, daughter, sister, friend and professional, and my life is crazy-busy, but I've found these to be simple, realistic ways to keep my stress levels in check. By making stress reduction a priority in my daily life, I'm eating, sleeping, moving, working and living a much better, more relaxed life than before. I'm able to be the best version of myself.

I want you to reach the same place.

*Less stress, more rest.*

# Stress and weight gain

It breaks my heart when women say to me, 'I'm doing all the right things. I'm eating well, exercising daily, and I've given up processed food – but my weight still isn't budging! Why?'

Straight away, I ask, 'How are your stress levels?' High stress means high cortisol, which affects hormonal balance.

Stress can prevent you from reaching your optimal, healthy weight. From a physical perspective, high cortisol levels are linked to lower thyroid function as well as weight gain, especially around the stomach area. Cortisol also throws off our blood sugar levels, which triggers cravings and overeating. Ever wondered why you eat more when you're stressed? Or crave chocolate? This could be why.

Some people lose their appetite when they're stressed, but then overeat later when their appetite returns. On the other hand, low cortisol levels occur when your stress levels have been high for a long time then crash in a spectacular fashion. That's the adrenal fatigue we talked about above.

In this low-energy state, it's harder to lose weight. You crave simple carbs and sugar to pick you up, and you definitely don't have the energy to exercise.

From an emotional point of view, I believe that when we worry and stress about our weight – as so many women and men do – we increase our cortisol levels, which can make weight loss more difficult. And, as we discovered in Chapter 2, hopping on the scales and riding the roller-coaster of emotions that comes with that can really increase our stress levels.

The takeaway? If you can learn how to manage your stress, you'll find that your weight will balance out naturally.

## The parasympathetic vs sympathetic nervous system

You may have heard of these two systems before. They are very important, and they need to be in balance in order for your body to respond to stress well.

The parasympathetic nervous system is responsible for the body's 'rest and digest' function. It works to calm the body. The sympathetic nervous system is responsible for the body's 'fight or flight' response. It controls how we react to perceived threats.

When we're stressed, the sympathetic nervous system steps in. Our heart rate increases, our blood presure increases, our muscles contract and adrenaline starts pumping. Basically, it shuts down any other systems that aren't essential for survival, like digestion.

When the 'danger' is gone, the parasympathetic nervous system takes over to bring us back into balance. Our heart rate steadies and our muscles relax.

These systems worked a treat in the early days, when the biggest threats for humans were wild animals and rival tribes. The sympathetic nervous system helped us in literal life-and-death situations, and the parasympathetic nervous system calmed us down once the threat had passed. But today, our stresses aren't as clearly defined. They're in our phones and email inboxes, demanding our attention, and they never really go away. As a result we're stressed to the point where our sympathetic nervous system never stops working, our systems are in overdrive, and it's neither healthy nor natural. We very rarely enter true rest or calm.

# How can we manage stress?

Let's move on to solutions! To keep your cortisol levels in check, you need to set boundaries. Boundaries are a big theme in this book (as you've probably noticed). For less stress and more rest, I swear by these eight strategies. I can easily incorporate them into my life, so I'm hoping you can do the same.

## 1 Schedule stress-free time every day

You've heard me say this again and again but, honestly, implementing the JSHealth Stress-Free Zone (SFZ) has drastically reduced my stress and anxiety, and I'll tell anyone who'll listen about it!

It's simple. Schedule 10–20 minutes of your day for silence, stillness and solitude, and focus on YOU and YOUR needs. (How divine does that sound?)

If you can commit to giving yourself this time to decompress and relax, you'll feel so much calmer. You'll even fall asleep faster, and stay asleep. I personally like to rest after my work day. But if you have kids, rest when they do, or rest when they're playing sport or watching TV.

### My stress-free time looks like this:

- I put my phone in another room.
- I put my legs up the wall for 10 minutes and breathe deeply. This is a pose borrowed from yoga, and it's brilliant for calming down the nervous system.
- Sometimes, I meditate to calming music or I go for a stroll outside.

Your stress-free time might look different from mine, or you might like to try the same activities. All I ask is that you do something that makes you feel happy and calm, and that you do it away from technology.

### Here are a few more ideas for how you could spend your 10–20 minutes (or more):

- Read a book.
- Soak in a bath.
- Have a nap.
- Light a candle and rest on the couch with a cuppa.
- Spend some time alone, being still and breathing deeply.

Remember to put your phone away (unless you're using a meditation app). Once you introduce the SFZ into your life, you'll never look back. You'll start looking forward to your rest, and also to how light and energised you'll feel afterwards. Try it today!

*\* Activity*

# CALM DOWN INSTANTLY WITH ALTERNATE NOSTRIL BREATHING

I learned this practice in India a few years ago, and now I do it twice a day – usually in the bath or before bed. I'm addicted! It's brilliant for relaxing the nervous system, and I don't know of another exercise that creates calm so quickly. Here's how to do it:

1   Press against one nostril with your finger so it closes.
2   Take a deep breath in from your nose, and then exhale.
3   Release and repeat with the other nostril, alternating for 1–2 minutes, or until you feel calm.

If you're a visual person, you can google instructional videos. And if this doesn't appeal to you, focus on doing ten to twenty deep belly breaths twice a day to calm your nervous system.

## Set social media boundaries

I want to reiterate how much calmer you'll feel if you limit your social media use. In today's hyper-connected world, the boundaries I listed on page 82 have had a huge impact on reducing my stress levels. I feel so much calmer when I switch off the screen. Flick back for a refresher if you need one.

## Exercise moderately, not insanely

A lot of research has been done on the dramatic effect that exercise can have on reducing stress and boosting our energy levels. Regular exercise makes me feel calmer, happier and more clear-headed, so I move my body daily. Most days, this includes my morning workout (see page 59), but I also like incidental exercise – taking the stairs instead of the lift, or walking instead of driving. If I'm on a call, I might walk up and down the street. Every little bit of movement counts. But, as you'll learn in this chapter, TOO much exercise can increase your cortisol levels and lower energy levels. So focus on 30 minutes of movement a day, and work out in ways you love. Don't force it. Do those two things, and you'll automatically feel less stressed!

## Don't buy into busyness

'Busyness' is a badge of honour these days. When people say, 'I'm soooo busy,' they are often looking for validation. I can get sucked into this too, but I'm trying to be more conscious of it and catch myself before commenting on my own busyness.

For years, I struggled with incorporating stillness into my everyday life. As JSHealth has evolved into a fully-fledged business, my responsibilities have grown. Every day I have a million thoughts and to-do lists running through my mind, and I'm constantly on the go. I love my work, and I'm very attached to it, so sometimes when I stop, I feel a bit lost. I feel anxious. I don't know what to do with myself.

Can you relate?

I believe this addiction to being busy impacts our mental health and energy levels.

So try to relieve the pressure you put on yourself to be busy all the time. Listen to what your body needs, speak to yourself with kindness, and step into stillness without guilt.

When we surrender to how we're truly feeling, life becomes easier. There's a time for work and a time for play. It's okay to take some time for yourself once in a while. It's okay to have a slow day. It's okay to sleep in without thinking you 'should' wake up and get going. It's okay not to respond to those emails for a few hours. It's okay to take a mental health day. It's okay to be still.

When I do, everything feels better.

## Say NO more often

This is a tricky one, but I promise it's worth it. I used to say yes all the time. To everything and everyone. I had the 'disease to please' – it's a real thing! FOMO (fear of missing out) is a real thing too.

Do these sound familiar?

I think they're responsible for many of us saying yes more than we'd like to. But this can take a toll on our health and wellbeing, because it adds stress to our lives without us even realising it.

Saying NO is actually a form of self-love and self-care.

Saying YES to absolutely everything can lead to unnecessary stress and anxiety.

Of course, there are caveats: at my core, I'm a yes person. I believe in saying yes in order to live a full and abundant life. I don't want to miss out on incredible opportunities, and I'm sure you feel the same.

So instead, I set boundaries and I say yes when doing so feels good in my gut. When my intuition tells me to do something, I do it. When I feel good about an offer, I take it. Saying yes to socialising when you're energetic and in the mood means you'll actually enjoy yourself, and you won't count down the minutes until you can leave.

THE 12-STEP MIND-BODY-FOOD RESET

## What's the rush?

Rushing is often associated with panic, and panic creates stress. When we rush, we don't breathe slowly and deeply, which is so important for restoring our nervous system, adrenal gland function and digestion.

If you're a known rusher, try to give yourself more time in the day. Wake up earlier, avoid jam-packing your day where possible, and say NO to unnecessary commitments more often.

Slowing down is one of my biggest challenges, but when I do it, it feels good. It makes me feel calmer. I realise that slowing down isn't always possible, but please do it when you can – especially if you catch yourself rushing for no reason.

When I'm tired or need some down time, I've become better at saying, 'Thank you, but I'm going to pass on that.' It's empowering and energising, and my friends understand. They know that we have plenty of time to be together, and they don't judge me.

The fact is, we all have a lot going on. Sometimes, a night in your PJs, with a home-cooked meal and Netflix is exactly what your mind, body and soul crave. Embrace that! It's so freeing.

It's unbelievable how much saying no can relieve stress. Please don't be afraid to try it!

## Get enough sleep

If you can prioritise getting between 7 and 9 hours of sleep each night, you'll not only feel calmer, you'll also be better able to manage your stress levels.

As someone who struggled with insomnia, I really empathise with anyone who deals with poor or broken sleep. It can be very debilitating. I know firsthand that a good night's sleep is a game changer.

If you're not sleeping well, here are my top tips for a good night's sleep. (And trust me, I've tried them all.)

- Switch social media and emails off by 9 pm at the latest.
- Put your phone in another room after dinner.
- Steer clear of caffeine (including green tea, black tea and matcha) after 11 am at the latest. (If you're a shiftworker, see page 136.)
- Create a relaxing night-time routine. See pages 138–39 for a detailed breakdown.
- Avoid intense exercise in the evenings.
- Eat a portion of protein at dinner. See Chapter 8 for dinner options that include protein and the other macronutrients.
- Drink chamomile tea before bed.
- Don't eat refined sugar, like chocolate or sweets, after dinner.

- Take magnesium glycinate under the guidance of a health practitioner. It's a miracle mineral for calming down the mind and nervous system, and you can get it in tablet or powder form.

If you can't fall asleep, put your legs up the wall for 10 minutes before bed and breathe deeply. It instantly calms down the nervous system and restores balance to the body and hormones after a long day. Give it a go! Don't worry, my husband thought I was nuts until he tried doing this himself!

## How to stay healthy as a shiftworker

Thanks to the unusual sleeping and eating patterns associated with shiftwork, it can be really challenging for shiftworkers to stick to a consistent plan and meet their health goals. Many shiftworkers struggle with poor or broken sleep, low energy, sugar cravings, high stress, and a reliance on caffeine and alcohol.

In addition to the other guidelines in this book, here are a few strategies to try:

- Avoid caffeine 8 hours before your next sleep, as it can stay in your bloodstream and keep you awake.
- Commit to getting between 7 and 8 hours of sleep, no matter what time of the day/night you get it. Your body needs this time to rest and repair. Set up a bedtime ritual that helps to calm down your nervous system before sleep.
- Eat a high-quality protein and a portion of good fat at every meal – especially at breakfast.
- Prepare protein-rich snacks for your shifts. It's so important to have a healthy snack handy, or else the vending machine becomes too tempting. See Chapter 9.
- Let go of the need to be perfect. There's no point putting pressure on yourself to make healthy choices all the time.
- Take magnesium glycinate before bed. It can relax your nervous system after a shift and prepare your body for sleep, no matter what time it is.

## Release the pressure you're putting on yourself

We put so much pressure on ourselves: pressure to eat perfectly, to exercise every day, to look good. Pressure to be the perfect partner, parent, friend, worker, sibling ... Pressure to do it all right. It's easy to beat ourselves up. And this can happen subconsciously. Thoughts like, 'I'm not good enough,' or 'I should be doing more,' pop up more than we might like to admit. These thoughts can manifest as physical stress and anxiety, which can affect our digestion and skin. Think about it; on days when you're stressed, does your skin break out? Does your digestion slow down? I know my systems become compromised when I'm stressed. Pressure can also be a precursor to emotional eating and binge eating. Everything is connected.

Relieve the pressure to do it all right and perfectly. Perfection doesn't exist. Instead, speak to yourself with kindness and care. This will reduce your stress, and help you to build a healthier relationship with yourself. To remind yourself how to do this, revisit Chapter 2.

## Adjust your diet for stress management

What you eat affects how you feel. To stay calm and steadily energised throughout the day, you need to keep your blood sugar levels balanced. When you're 'hangry', you're more anxious, irritable and stressed.

When we consume too much caffeine, carbs and refined sugar, we experience blood sugar drops, which can trigger anxiety, stress and low energy. On the flipside, if you enjoy foods that support and balance your blood sugars, you'll feel more in control of your body throughout the day. You'll make healthier choices because eating well makes you feel good.

In Chapter 3, we covered the importance of eating all the macronutrients, and focusing on wholefoods rather than processed foods. Eating food as close to their natural state as possible gives your body the fuel it needs to combat stress. It also makes you feel better overall.

Of course, I'm all about eating well most of the time, and treating yourself when you wish. Balance is the key to a healthy life.

# A relaxing night-time routine is a must for stress reduction

Along with the eight strategies I've just outlined, I have one more powerful stress-busting tool to share with you: my calming evening routine on page 138. This routine has allowed me to unwind and let go of the day's stresses. But it wasn't always this way.

A few years ago, my evenings looked like this: I'd eat a 'diet' or low-calorie dinner – and not very mindfully. I'd feel guilty about every bite, and be distracted by my negative thoughts or whatever was on TV. I had a lot of anxiety around mealtimes, which would often cause me to overeat or trigger a binge later on. I was addicted to my phone and computer, and would scroll, text and compare myself to people on social media until 11 pm. I'd succumb to late-night snacking on 'healthy' or 'fat-free' foods that were usually high in sugar or artificial sweeteners. Then I'd watch TV until midnight. Finally, I'd go to bed. But I'd often wake up in the middle of the night and check my phone, which was right next to me on my bedside table. After a night of broken sleep, I'd wake up in the morning, anxious and exhausted.

Not anymore. Now I cherish my evenings just as much as my mornings, and I try not to let anything get in the way of an evening of divine self-care after a busy day at work. It calms me down, motivates me to work harder during the day, improves my sleep and I wake up feeling energised and ready for the day ahead.

# MY EVENING ROUTINE

This routine is a lifesaver and will help you reclaim the day, relax and reflect. I'd love for you to create your own night-time routine. Your rituals don't have to be the same as mine, and they don't have to be done perfectly every night, but a few elements of my routine may resonate with you. Trust me when I say it's a beautiful way to end a day! Starting tonight, I want you to take the time to unwind. I want you to go to bed feeling like you've done something for yourself.

## Start dinner

**Between 6.30 and 7 pm**
I finish work for the day. I head to the kitchen and cook a healthy dinner for me and my husband, Dean. It's not fancy or fussy, and because I've stocked up and prepped some food on Sunday, these meals don't take me longer than 20–30 minutes to make. (See Chapter 8 for my quick and easy dinner ideas, or head over to my Instagram @jshealth.)

## Last-minute messages

While I'm making dinner, I attend to any last messages, emails or calls.

## Dinner's ready!

I plate up our food, sit down with Dean, and eat slowly, mindfully and with so much joy. What's the rush?

## Set my boundaries

We clean up together, and this is when I set my tried-and-tested boundaries for good sleep and high energy the next day. Around 8 pm I delete the social media apps from my phone. As I mentioned on page 85, this one small practice has worked wonders to lower my stress levels – try it! I plug my phone into a charger away from my bedroom, and I switch all other tech devices off, including my laptop, before placing them in another room too. At this point, I stop talking and thinking about work. I have the whole next day to work hard and be creative.

## Stress-free zone

The bliss begins! I pop my legs up against the wall and breathe deeply for 5–10 minutes. It calms my nervous system and brings my stress levels down. If you struggle to fall asleep quickly, give this a go.

## Herbal tea (or sweet treat!)

I sip on herbal tea or a decaf chai tea with warm almond milk and cinnamon. A couple of times a week, I'll savour one of my favourite sweet treats (see Chapter 11), and I enjoy every single bite.

## Relax

I soak in a bath with lavender oil, watch an episode of my favourite TV show or read a book.

## Supplements

I pop a multi-strain probiotic and take magnesium glycinate, to prepare my body for sleep.

## Sleep

Around 10 pm, I fall into a deep sleep.

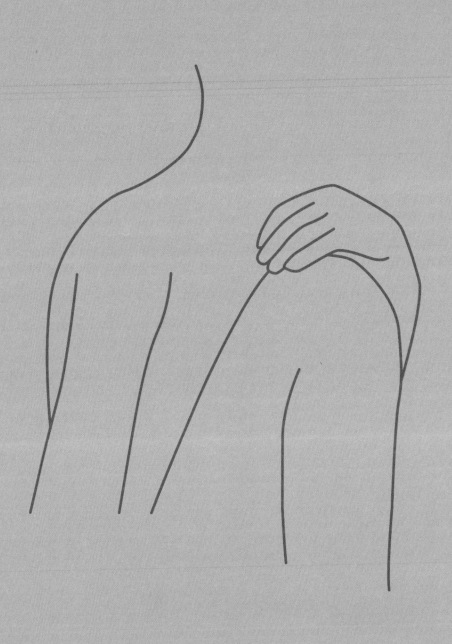

# 8

# Spend 20 minutes making dinner. That's it!

---

*I refuse to spend a lot of time in the kitchen making dinner after a long, tiring day. You don't have to either!*

# The truth? I don't spend much time cooking

If you follow my work or follow me on Instagram, you may assume that I spend hours and hours cooking healthy food. After all, I'm a nutritionist! But this is only the case when I'm shooting recipes for work.

In my everyday life, I spend very little time in the kitchen. The reason? I don't actually enjoy cooking that much (shocking, I know!). But let me explain: I love experimenting and creating healthy meals that nourish my body – I live for it! However, I'm an impatient and busy person, and I find it frustrating to slave away in the kitchen all day. I have other things to do.

Many people have a perception that healthy food is bland, expensive or hard to make, so I'm on a mission to prove them wrong. This is why I founded JSHealth in the first place. I wanted to show how easy, simple and fuss-free healthy cooking could be. Once you learn how to whip up healthy, nourishing food quickly and with ease, you'll never turn back. Fast, nutritious food is the key to maintaining the healthy life in the long term, for both you and your family. Read on, and you won't have to spend hours in your kitchen to achieve that.

## How to cook good food, quickly!

I'm short on time, and I'm sure you are too.

I really empathise with busy parents, workers and students, and I understand the struggle. As my business has grown, my time has become increasingly limited. While this growth has been an adjustment, I'm grateful for it, as it's helped me to connect with my community, and speak to people who want to be healthy but just don't have a lot of spare time. If you're nodding your head, don't worry. I always have you in mind when I'm creating wholesome and easy-to-follow recipes.

When it comes to cooking quickly, I have to thank my mum, because she's my cooking inspiration, and the one who taught me how to cook quick, easy and downright delicious meals. To this day, she works full time and arrives home at 6.30 pm. By 7.15 pm, she's put together the most delicious and abundant meal for the family. It's amazing, and she's become famous for it among family and friends! She never compromised on taste, and she never spent hours in the kitchen. I definitely learned some of my best tricks from her.

Here's the exciting news: you can cook fast meals too!

Over the last few years, I've had even less time to cook so I've come up with recipes, meal ideas and prepping tricks that save SO much time and

*Spend 20 minutes making dinner. That's it!*

stress. You may be familiar with some of them if you've read my first two books.

I want to share those tips with you now.

## Cut down on your prep time on weekdays

For a lot of people, cooking isn't the issue, it's the prepping – that's the part that's time-consuming. And I get it. After a day of work, who wants to head to the kitchen and work even more? No one! That's why I wrote a whole chapter on prep! Getting on top of the prep aspect of cooking is the key to unlocking so many quick meals.

To make your weekday dinners quick and easy, it helps to have a few prepping strategies up your sleeve. Along with all those outlined in Chapter 6, here are a few more of my favourite day-to-day prep tips.

1    Plan your meals for the first 3 nights of the week. Mapping out your meals for the beginning of the week means one less decision you have to make. That's why I like to buy all the essentials I need on a Sunday, so when dinnertime rolls around, I have everything ready to go. Sometimes, I'll buy my protein after work, or ask Dean to swing by the shops on his way home. Of course, you can change your plans to suit your mood. For example, if it's a cold, stormy day and you planned to eat a salad for dinner, you can switch to a homemade soup instead. I'm all about flexibility.

2    If you find yourself with 10 extra minutes in the morning, pre-chop some veggies or marinate some meat for dinner – anything to streamline the process later.

3    Invest in kitchen equipment that helps you to be more efficient, like a food processor to slice and dice for you, or a spiraliser to make veggie noodles in minutes.

4    Turn to cooking methods that support quick meals, such as roasting on high heat, stir-frying and grilling. See pages 146–51 for some of my favourite fast cooking techniques. Slow cookers can also be wonderful for busy days. Spending just 15 minutes in the morning prepping ingredients to throw in your slow cooker can mean coming home to a delicious, generous, hearty meal that needs nothing more than to be served up with a sprinkle of salt and pepper.

5    Enlist a buddy. Cooking up a storm with your partner, friend or older child is not only faster, but it makes the whole process a lot more fun.

6   Finally, keep things simple. A fast meal is not a complicated meal. Think fresh ingredients dressed up with condiments, herbs and spices from your 'flavour tray' (see page 92). Add some heat, and that's your job done. Save complicated techniques and time-intensive recipes for the weekends.

# My guide to making no-fuss meals

The go-to dinner options in this chapter contain all the macronutrients (see Chapter 3 for a refresher) and they take just 20 minutes or less to make! They're part of my one-pan series, which is exactly what it sounds like. One pan = less work, and less cleaning.

## How to make healthy meals taste good

As I always say, eating is one of life's simplest pleasures – so our food has to taste good! Flavouring healthy meals is easier than you may think.

This is what I use:

- Freshly chopped herbs. I love sprinkling chopped parsley, basil or mint on my meals. It adds a fresh, delicious taste, and I can't get enough.
- Curry powder. I add this tangy spice to almost all cooked meals. It really lifts the flavour of dishes such as cauliflower rice, veggie mash and soups. Try it!
- Himalayan salt and black pepper. A sprinkle of these makes every savoury dish taste better. Himalayan salt is natural, unprocessed and contains important trace minerals for good health.
- Fresh lemon juice. I love lemon, so I squeeze this over everything!
- Dijon mustard and tahini. These are great alternatives to mayo, and I incorporate them into my dressings and sauces.
- Mixed herbs and spices. I buy these prepackaged mixes from the health-food store. My favourites are: Moroccan spice mix, Cajun spice mix, cinnamon, cumin, curry powder, paprika and turmeric.
- Nutritional yeast. I sprinkle this dairy-free delight over stir-fries, soups and salads for a cheesy taste.
- Pesto. I love making my own pesto! It's a great topping for healthy pastas or salads.

# Veggie cooking methods

The veggie cooking ideas on this page to page 151 are great to turn to when you're in quick-cooking mode and looking for some inspiration. Add your favourite protein to the mix and, voilà! Dinner is done.

VEGGIE COOKING METHOD ONE

## Stir-frying

Stir-frying is done by using a wok over a very high heat and for minimal cooking times. Stir-frying works best when you have all of your ingredients prepared and ready for use before you preheat your wok, as the overall cooking will be completed in 5 minutes and requires close attention when such high heat is used. The vegetables always remain tender-crisp and keep their vibrant colours when stir-fried. Simply combine the ingredients below with your protein of choice and a side of cooked quinoa or brown rice.

### Try these stir-frying combinations

**1** **Garlic soy:** 1 tablespoon coconut oil + 3 sliced garlic cloves + 4 halved baby bok choy + 2 tablespoons tamari (gluten-free soy sauce)

**2** **Miso ginger:** 1 tablespoon coconut oil + 2 tablespoons ginger cut into thin matchsticks + 2 teaspoons miso paste + 1 chopped eggplant + 2 sliced spring onions

**3** **Curry spiced:** 1 tablespoon coconut oil + 2 crushed garlic cloves + 1 teaspoon curry powder + 2 cups chopped mixed vegetables (cauliflower, broccoli, carrot, celery, zucchini) + 2 tablespoons water

# Grilling

Grilled foods come with those characteristic marks on the food.
The heat source for grilling always comes from the bottom and can
either be achieved by using an open-flame, such as a barbecue, or
from a chargrill pan that has been preheated on a stovetop.

## Try these grilling combinations

**1** Thin slices of pumpkin sprayed with coconut oil cooking
spray and coated in sesame seeds and a sprinkling of
cinnamon. Served with a little drizzle of pure maple syrup.

**2** Torn kale leaves sprayed with coconut oil cooking spray and
lightly drizzled with lemon juice. Served drizzled with
a little hulled tahini.

**3** Thickly sliced onions and mixed-coloured capsicums
tossed in balsamic vinegar, rosemary leaves and a drizzle
of cold-pressed extra virgin olive oil.

# Roasting

Roasting is done by using higher temperatures in a preheated oven and gives an all-round heat source, providing even cooking with great browning. If you get your oven nice and hot while you do some chopping, you can have a tray of deliciousness on the table in around 15–20 minutes.

## Preheat your oven to 180–200°C and

## try these roasting combinations

1   Toss halved brussels sprouts with cold-pressed extra-virgin olive oil, crushed garlic cloves and baby tomatoes, then roast for 20–25 minutes. Serve with lemon wedges.

2   Toss chopped orange sweet potato and chopped red onion with cold-pressed extra virgin olive oil, dried mixed herbs and whole natural almonds, then roast for 20 minutes. Serve with chopped flat-leaf parsley.

3   Toss cauliflower and broccoli florets with cold-pressed extra virgin olive oil and curry powder, then roast for 20 minutes. Serve with coriander leaves and lime wedges.

# So you're going out for dinner?

I cook 5 days a week and eat out the rest. But I've learned how to make good food choices when I'm out, and you can too.

I find I have better digestion, skin and energy when I eat food I've prepared myself. Nothing beats home-cooked meals! But I also absolutely love eating out on the weekends (and sometimes, one night during the week too). I'm a foodie through and through – I don't let my healthy life affect that.

Once upon a time, healthy options were few and far between. But now, it's easy to make a healthy choice when you're dining out, and enjoy every bite. I have healthy dining down to an art. When I eat out, I order a clean, nutritious main meal, but I'm balanced and flexible. So I'll leave room for moderate and mindful indulgence. I might sip on wine, dip some freshly baked bread in olive oil, or savour a few bites of a shared dish that's not particularly healthy. I usually try a dessert too. A couple of spoonfuls tend to hit the spot, but there are times when I'll go all out and order my own. I don't deny myself. If I feel like something, I'll get it, savour it, and then move on with zero guilt. (We'll be chatting more about this in Chapter 11.) By giving myself room to move and permission to indulge, I'm more motivated to stick to the healthy life. That's balance.

## Dining out the healthy way

'Jess, I've been invited to a party. How should I eat?' As a nutritionist, I get asked this question all the time, and my answer is always: go with the best choices available to you. At dinner parties, events and weddings, you won't have as much control over the food, so all you can do is work with what you're offered – while allowing yourself a little leeway!

We can absolutely still enjoy our social lives, and go to the party, drink alcohol and eat delicious food without compromising our health goals. So my best advice is try not to be fussy in social situations. It's not fun to refuse to eat anything at a dinner party, or to skip it altogether because of your dietary concerns. That rigidity will only make you more anxious.

Whether you're at a party or going to a restaurant, here are my tips for dining out in a healthier way. Give these a try the next time you're out and I bet you'll feel better for it.

> You can be *healthy* AND *social*, so go to the *party*!

- **Never arrive at a party or a restaurant starving.** I always eat a protein-rich snack around 4 or 5 pm (more on this in the next chapter!). It gives me a boost of steady energy and keeps me full, so I can stay more in control of my food choices later on. If you're famished, you'll find it harder to order well or turn down that second round of canapés. I know a lot of people who avoid eating all day when they know they're going out, and this often leads to overeating at dinnertime. How can it not?

- **Reduce simple carbs such as white bread, rice, pasta and potatoes.** I find these make me feel tired and sluggish, which isn't great when I'm trying to socialise! I go for the wholegrain options and steer clear of the carb-heavy foods. That being said, give yourself permission to indulge in any of those foods if you're in the mood. This isn't gospel – it's a general guide to making healthy choices.

- **Start with a fresh salad or bowl of veggies.** This fills me up, and gives me a hit of fibre and nutrients, which mean I'm less likely to go for the heaviest main. If a party is buffet style, load your plate up with protein and veggies first, as these are the most satiating macronutrients.

- **Check out the sides and starters.** Most restaurants list their cleanest, freshest options on these sections of the menu. I usually order a side of steamed or grilled veggies to pair with my main meal.

- **Opt for the grilled, steamed, roasted and baked options.** My golden rule is to steer clear of fried options, because fried foods make me feel sick.

- **Try to build a healthy meal in your mind.** When I'm ordering, I make sure I include all the macronutrients: a healthy protein, a good fat, a complex carb and loads of veggies for fibre. I don't skip any. If my main doesn't have one of these macronutrients, I'll order a side. By doing this, I know that I'll leave the meal feeling full and satiated. See pages 48–49 for tips on how to build a healthy meal.

- **Stop at two or three alcoholic drinks.** Avoid added fruit juice, mixers and cocktails – they're loaded with sugar, and chances are you'll feel awful the next day. Instead, sip on vodka, tequila or gin mixed with soda, fresh lime, cucumber slices or coconut water. And go for red wine over white wine, if possible. Finally, drink slowly. What's the rush? Drinking less will probably mean you'll eat less, as alcohol dulls our senses and inhibits our decision-making.

- **If it's a potluck, bring a healthy dish!** Inspire your friends and family by whipping up a delicious and nutritious contribution. They'll love it! This chapter is filled with some of my favourite dishes that are perfect for a potluck.

- **Finally, be social and flexible.** Try not to be fussy or overly worried about your eating choices. The healthy life is about balance, and socialising is a part of that. And our bodies can handle decadent foods in moderate amounts. So try the dessert, eat that birthday cake or sip on a glass of champagne. Just practise portion control. Remember, our body listens to what we do most of the time, so relax and enjoy your social life. Eat that pizza or pasta with zero guilt.

Don't deny yourself. Try a little of everything in moderation. I love trying new foods and dishes, and I'll never let my healthy life get in the way of that. Because, balance.

# Roast Moroccan chickpeas and pumpkin with lime yoghurt

**GF**    **DF**    **VEG**    **VEGAN**

**SERVES** 4
**PREP** 20 MINUTES
**COOK** 20 MINUTES

———

60 ml (¼ cup) cold-pressed
    extra-virgin olive oil
2 tablespoons dried Moroccan
    spice mix
1 x 400 g tin chickpeas, drained
    and rinsed well
400 g butternut pumpkin,
    peeled, seeded and cut into
    thin (5 mm) chips
200 g brussels sprouts, sliced
    into rounds
50 g (½ cup) pecans
1 cup (firmly packed) baby
    spinach leaves

**LIME YOGHURT**
200 g (¾ cup) coconut yoghurt
zest and juice of 1 large lime
1 tablespoon finely chopped
    fresh mint leaves
sea salt and freshly ground
    black pepper

1    Preheat the oven to 200°C (180°C fan-forced). Line a large baking tray with non-stick baking paper.

2    Make the lime yoghurt first by combining all of the ingredients. Taste and adjust seasoning if needed then refrigerate until ready to serve.

3    Place the oil, spice mix, chickpeas, pumpkin, sprouts and pecans in a large bowl and toss well to coat in the oil and spices. Spread this mixture evenly in the prepared tray then bake for 20 minutes, or until the vegetables are tender and golden.

4    Once everything is cooked, remove the tray from the oven and add the spinach. Toss until well combined and the leaves start to wilt.

5    Take the tray straight to the table and dollop generous spoonfuls of lime yoghurt around the tray before serving.

# Chicken, broccolini and quinoa pilaf

**GF**

**SERVES** 4
**PREP** 15 MINUTES
**COOK** 20 MINUTES

———

2 tablespoons cold-pressed
    extra-virgin olive oil
600 g lean chicken breast fillet,
    cut into 1½ cm pieces
2 garlic cloves, crushed
1 large red onion, finely chopped
200 g (1 cup) quinoa, rinsed very
    well and drained
500 ml (2 cups) chicken stock
135 g (1 bunch) broccolini,
    trimmed and halved
    lengthways
20 g (¼ cup) shaved parmesan
lemon wedges, to serve

1   Heat a flameproof baking dish or casserole dish over high heat and add the oil, chicken, garlic and onion. Cook, stirring constantly, for 1 minute or until the garlic is fragrant.

2   Add the quinoa and stock and stir well, making sure that all of the quinoa grains are submerged in the stock. Immediately cover the dish with a lid and reduce the heat to medium-low. Simmer with the lid on for 15 minutes, or until the chicken is cooked through and the quinoa has absorbed all of the stock.

3   Remove the dish from the heat, immediately add the broccolini and put the lid back on. Take the dish to the table, allowing it to stand for 3 minutes so the broccolini can steam lightly. When ready to dish up, sprinkle with parmesan and pepper and serve with lemon wedges.

Chicken, broccolini
and quinoa pilaf

*page 155*

# Barramundi with lentils and fennel

GF    DF

**SERVES** 4
**PREP** 15 MINUTES
**COOK** 20 MINUTES

————

2 tablespoons cold-pressed
    extra-virgin olive oil
1 leek, white and light green
    parts only, finely sliced into
    rounds and washed
2 baby fennel bulbs, trimmed
    and finely sliced lengthways
2 garlic cloves, crushed
1 x 400 g tin lentils, drained and
    rinsed well
500 ml (2 cups) chicken stock
4 x 150 g pieces of barramundi,
    skin and bones removed
135 g (1 cup) frozen baby peas
sea salt and freshly ground
    black pepper
½ handful of small mint leaves
½ handful of small basil leaves

1   Heat the oil in a large, deep non-stick frying pan over medium heat. Add the leek, fennel and garlic and cook, stirring occasionally, for 5 minutes or until the vegetables are starting to soften.

2   Add the lentils and the stock, and stir until the mixture comes to a simmer. Place the pieces of fish on top of the mixture and scatter over the peas. Simmer, partially covered with a lid, for 8–10 minutes, or until the fish and vegetables are just cooked and the stock has reduced down by three-quarters.

3   Take the pan straight to table, season well with salt and pepper and scatter over the mint and basil leaves before serving.

# Grilled crispy-skinned salmon and vegetables with tahini dressing

**GF**  **DF**

**SERVES** 4
**PREP** 20 MINUTES
**COOK** 10 MINUTES

———

4 x 150 g salmon fillets, skin on
sea salt
4 kale leaves, leaves torn, thick
    stems discarded
2 bunches thin green asparagus,
    woody ends removed
1 small lemon, finely sliced into
    rounds
freshly ground black pepper
2 tablespoons cold-pressed
    extra-virgin olive oil
1 tablespoon flaked almonds,
    toasted, to serve

**TAHINI DRESSING**
1 tablespoon cold-pressed
    extra-virgin olive oil
2 lemons, juiced
1 tablespoon tahini
½ teaspoon ground cumin
½ teaspoon dried chilli flakes
1–2 tablespoons warm water
sea salt and freshly ground
    black pepper

1  Preheat the oven grill to high. Line a large baking tray with foil.

2  Place the salmon fillets on the prepared tray, skin side up. Pat the skin dry with paper towel before seasoning it well with sea salt. Add the kale to the tray, making sure it sits in and around the salmon fillets. Next, arrange the asparagus on top of the salmon and kale, and finally, top with the lemon slices. Season everything well with salt and pepper and drizzle the vegetables (but not the salmon) with the oil.

3  Place the tray under the oven grill for 10 minutes, or until the salmon skin is crispy, the fish is just cooked and the vegetables are just tender.

4  While the salmon and vegetables cook, make the tahini dressing by whisking all the ingredients together in a bowl. Season well and then set aside until ready to serve.

5  Take the tray of salmon and veg straight to table and spoon the tahini dressing evenly over the vegetables on the tray (not the salmon, as you want that skin to stay nice and crispy). Serve hot, sprinkled with the almonds.

Grilled crispy-skinned salmon and vegetables with tahini dressing

page 159

# Lentil and sweet potato cottage pie

**GF**  **VEG**

**SERVES** 4
**PREP** 10 MINUTES
**COOK** 10 MINUTES

———

1 portion of Vegan lentil
    bolognese (page 122)
1 portion of Curried sweet
    potato mash (page 113)
1 tablespoon cold-pressed
    extra-virgin olive oil
shaved parmesan, to serve
basil leaves, to serve

1   Preheat the oven grill to high.

2   Reheat the bolognese then spoon into a 6-cup capacity flameproof baking dish and spread it around the dish evenly.

3   Top with the mash, using a fork to spread the mash evenly over the bolognese. Drizzle all over with the oil.

4   Cook under the grill for 5–8 minutes, or until the mash is golden and the sauce is bubbling up from underneath.

5   Take straight to the table and sprinkle some shaved parmesan and basil over the top before serving.

## To make it vegan and dairy-free ...

Serve without the shaved parmesan.

# Chargrilled beef with chilli pesto dressing

**GF**　**DF**

**SERVES** 4
**PREP** 20 MINUTES
**COOK** 10 MINUTES

————

4 x 180 g lean beef eye fillet
　　steaks, well seasoned
sea salt and freshly ground
　　black pepper
300 g baby squash, halved
　　crossways
400 g mixed baby heirloom
　　tomatoes, halved
100 g baby spinach leaves
80 g (½ cup) whole natural
　　almonds, toasted and
　　chopped

**CHILLI PESTO DRESSING**
2 teaspoons wholegrain mustard
½ teaspoon dried chilli flakes
1 garlic clove
60 ml (¼ cup) red wine vinegar
2 tablespoons cold-pressed
　　extra-virgin olive oil
small handful of basil leaves

1　Make the dressing first by blitzing all of the ingredients in a small food processor until well combined and smooth. Season well with salt and pepper, then set aside until ready to serve.

2　Meanwhile, preheat a large, deep chargrill pan.

3　Add the steaks and squash onto the chargrill pan. Cook for 3 minutes, turn the steaks over, then cook for another 3 minutes for medium steaks (cook for less time or for longer depending on how you like your meat cooked). Transfer the steaks to a board, cover with foil and allow to rest. Return the pan to the heat, add the tomatoes to the pan with the squash and cook for 3 minutes.

4　Remove the pan from the heat and add the baby spinach and almonds, tossing until everything is well combined and the spinach is starting to wilt. Season well with salt and pepper and then divide between the serving plates.

5　Slice the steaks thinly then arrange the slices on top of each serving of vegetables. Drizzle with the chilli pesto dressing and serve.

**Chargrilled beef
with chilli
pesto dressing**
*page 163*

## Tip

This meal is also delicious served with the Curried sweet potato mash (page 113).

# Creamy pea and broccoli pasta

**GF**   **DF**   **VEG**   **VEGAN**

**SERVES** 2
**PREP** 15 MINUTES
**COOK** 10 MINUTES

———

1 x 200 g packet mung bean
    fettuccine
120 g (2 cups) broccoli florets,
    roughly chopped
130 g (1 cup) frozen baby peas
1 x 400 g tin coconut cream
2 garlic cloves, crushed
handful of basil leaves, plus
    extra to serve
sea salt and freshly ground
    black pepper
dried chilli flakes, to serve

1   Bring a very large saucepan of water to the boil over high heat, then reduce the heat to low.

2   Add the fettuccine, broccoli and peas to the boiling water. Cook, stirring very gently and occasionally, for 6–8 minutes, or until the pasta is just cooked. Drain the pasta and vegetables.

3   Return the same pan to high heat and add the coconut cream, garlic and basil leaves. Cook for 2 minutes, or until the sauce thickens slightly. Remove the pan from the heat and add the fettuccine mixture back to the pan, tossing gently to coat everything in the cream mixture.

4   Divide the pasta between large serving bowls and season well with salt and pepper. Serve topped with extra basil leaves and some dried chilli, if desired.

# Sticky sweet potato with sesame greens

**GF** **DF** **VEG** **VEGAN**

**SERVES** 2
**PREP** 20 MINUTES
**COOK** 20 MINUTES

———

1 tablespoon honey

60 ml (¼ cup) tamari (gluten-free
soy sauce)

1 teaspoon sesame oil

1 tablespoon cold-pressed
extra-virgin olive oil

350 g orange sweet potato,
finely sliced into rounds

1 red onion, cut into thin wedges

freshly ground black pepper

4 baby bok choy, halved
lengthways

2 field mushrooms, cleaned and
halved lengthways

40 g (¼ cup) whole natural
almonds, chopped

1 tablespoon sesame seeds

coriander sprigs, to serve

lime wedges, to serve

1  Preheat the oven to 200°C (180°C fan-forced). Place
a heavy-based baking dish in the oven to heat up.

2  Combine the honey, tamari, oils, sweet potato and onion
in a bowl, and grind over some pepper.

3  Carefully remove the hot baking dish from the preheated
oven and place the bok choy and mushrooms in the
dish. Add 2 tablespoons of water and then scatter the
honey vegetable mixture all around the dish.

4  Return the dish to the oven and roast for 15 minutes,
then add the almonds and sesame seeds and roast for
5 minutes more.

5  Take the dish straight to table and scatter over
coriander leaves before serving with lime wedges.

## To serve

Add your protein of choice to the dish to make it a complete meal.

**Sticky sweet potato
with sesame greens**

*page 167*

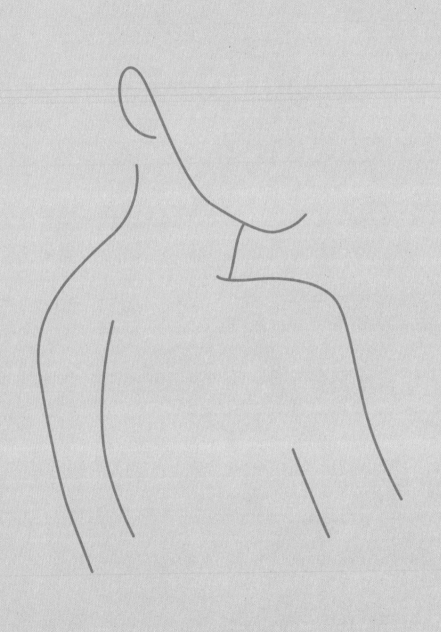

# 9

# Combat sugar cravings, for life

---

*I eat a protein-rich snack every day between 4 and 5 pm. This little trick has helped to reduce my cravings in a BIG way.*

# Cut down on what doesn't serve you

As a nutritionist, I've studied and observed how different foods affect our health. I've confirmed that there are two types of foods that we could all benefit from cutting down on to feel our best: refined sugar and gluten. From clinical experience, I've seen how much lighter, brighter and better people feel when they start reducing their intake of these foods. And the biggest difference I've noticed? People who cut back on these foods have more energy – and that, in itself, is life-changing. Remember, you can still absolutely enjoy these foods – it's just about reducing your intake.

When we have energy, we're more motivated to make better food choices, and to live a more active lifestyle. Eating less refined sugar and gluten also reduces bloating (which makes us feel much more comfortable), and it can help with weight balance in the long term.

If you've been on a health journey for a while, you might have been told to give up sugar by a nutritionist (or a few of them!). But in my opinion, it's unfair of us nutritionists to encourage you to quit sugar without explaining why you may be craving it in the first place, and how you'll benefit from giving it up.

It's not as simple as saying, 'Cut out sugar'; to reduce sugar intake properly – and for life – specific physical aspects, like gut health, blood sugar balance and stress, need to be addressed. Your diet also determines how easy or difficult it will be to cut down on sugar.

Don't worry. I'm here to help you manage this. As you know by now, I'm all about balance – no extremes and no restriction. So don't stress about cutting back on sugar and gluten completely. You'll still be able to enjoy gelato, eat toast for breakfast and indulge in desserts on the weekend. In fact, you should! This will help you to build a healthier relationship with food. It's just important that you become conscious of how these foods make you feel.

> **Your body won't go into panic mode if you indulge occasionally. Focus on making** *healthy choices* **most of the time. That's what matters.**
>
> *Remember that*

This chapter is going to help you take back control of your cravings. If you're a slave to sugar, I'm going to help you get to a point where sugar no

longer has the same power over you. You won't want eat an entire tub of ice cream – because savouring one scoop will be enough. It's so liberating.

Ready to combat your cravings once and for all?

## Let's talk about energy for a second

'I'm so *tired*. I have no *energy*.'

I hear this complaint all the time, and I have deep empathy for those who constantly feel run-down – especially those who wake up tired. When we're tired, everything feels harder. Life and healthy choices become much harder.

In my experience, the following factors may explain why you're feeling fatigued:

- You're eating too much refined sugar. (Hang in there; we'll take care of this soon.)
- You're drinking two to three cups of coffee a day.
- You're not enjoying balanced, satiating meals that keep your blood sugar levels in check. See Chapter 3 to remedy this.
- You've been stressed for as long as you can remember, and you may even be burnt out. See Chapter 7 for my (realistic and effective) stress-relief strategies.
- You're running on adrenaline most of the time. You're a rusher.
- You're a late-night snacker who mostly reaches for sweets. If you wake up tired, this could be the reason.
- You're consuming too much gluten, wheat and refined carbs. These foods zap energy. Try cutting down on them for a week and you'll notice a difference!
- Your gut isn't in great shape.

If any of these ring true for you, it's going to be okay! I'm going to guide you back to a place where you feel energised again.

# My top sugar-busting strategies

I know that my guide to giving up sugar for life (and with ease) really works, and I promise it's going to help you feel more energised too.

I'm not going to ask you to cut out sugar 'cold turkey'. Instead, I'm going to work with you to address the factors and things going on in your body that are fuelling your sugar cravings. If you can work on those, you'll be able to give up sugar much more easily, and get your energy back.

## 1 Enjoy a protein-rich snack between 4 and 5 pm

Of all my strategies, this one is the BIGGEST game changer. Eating more in the late afternoon will help you to eat less in the evening.

So many dieters don't snack because they believe it's bad for their waistline. In reality, and from my experience, this approach backfires. Skipping an afternoon snack leaves a big gap between main meals, and this is why many people end up overeating before or after dinner. They're starving! Their energy stores are low.

That's the first issue.

The second is that a lot of people snack on fruit or carbs in the afternoon because they need an energy boost, which isn't always the best choice. I've seen many clients struggle to combat their sugar cravings in the afternoon and post-dinner for this reason. If you tend to crave sugar later in the day, you may be able to trace it back to fruit.

As we've discussed, protein is one of the most important macronutrients. It's satiating and filling, and our body needs it to function at its peak. By enjoying a protein-rich snack at this time of day (rather than anything you can get your hands on), you'll balance out your blood sugar levels, and boost your mood and energy, and you'll feel full. As a result, you won't be tempted to graze as much (especially when you get home from work). And when dinnertime rolls around, you'll feel much more in control of your food choices, and you'll be less likely to give in to that post-dinner sweet tooth.

The power of a protein-rich snack really is amazing. You won't need to reach for sugar (think chocolate, lollies or sugary drinks) to perk you up because you'll have busted your cravings. Your weight will be easier to manage too.

So please don't be afraid of making this late-afternoon snack part of your daily routine. If you're going to be out and about at work or school, pack a healthy snack before you leave home; I never leave the house without one tucked in my bag.

The key is never to let yourself get too hungry, as that's when you tend to make poor food decisions. Fighting hunger pangs isn't healthy.

# Quick protein-rich snacks to curb your sugar cravings

*Pack a snack tomorrow.*

*I bet it will help.*

Carrot sticks with 1 tablespoon of almond butter

Homemade trail mix including 25 g broken 80% dark chocolate, 2 tablespoons of goji berries and 1 tablespoon of toasted flaked coconut

1 cup of roasted cauliflower florets, 2 tablespoons of ricotta and 1 tablespoon of Pistachio dukkah *page 190*

150–200 g Greek yoghurt with cinnamon, vanilla stevia and 1 tablespoon of protein powder (optional)

1 boiled egg drizzled with 2 teaspoons of the Moroccan tahini dressing *page 119*

Veggie sticks with 2 tablespoons of hummus or tahini

Celery sticks with 1 tablespoon of peanut butter

¼ cup of raw nuts and a sliced carrot

## Give your gut some love

The state of your digestive system influences your sugar cravings. Specifically, it impacts your blood sugar levels – and research backs this up. Scientists have found a direct connection between our blood sugar levels and gut bacteria.

For good gut health, we need a balance of good and bad microflora (gut bacteria).

Unfortunately, for many of us, sugar, gluten and processed foods eat away at the good bacteria, and the bad bugs start to overrun the gut.

Sugar actually feeds the bad bugs in the gut. When our microflora is out of balance, we end up with dysbiosis, which means the gastrointestinal tract is compromised. This can cause an upset stomach, inflammation, cravings, flatulence, fatigue, constipation, and even autoimmune conditions and irritable bowl syndrome (IBS).

This is why gut health is so important. When your gut is in good shape, you'll naturally crave less sugar – and you'll feel lighter, brighter and better overall.

Gluten is a two-part protein found in grains – mainly wheat, rye and barley. It's called a 'sticky' protein because it holds together the nutrient stores of the plant (which explains why it's often used to bind together processed foods). The main gluten sources in our diet are breads, cereals, cakes, biscuits and crackers. But gluten is often hidden in unexpected places, like shop-bought gravies, soups, sausages, bottled sauces and some marinades.

For many people, gluten causes gut irritation and inflammation. If you suffer from gut issues, I strongly suggest you try cutting out gluten for 3 weeks, then slowly reintroducing it into your diet. If you discover that you felt better without gluten (or worse when you start eating it again), then it's probably causing problems for you.

I personally avoid gluten because I've noticed I have much more energy when I don't eat it.

### Gut-friendly tips

♥ Add 2 g of glutamine to your smoothies. It's great for sealing the gut lining and reducing negative gut symptoms.
♥ For an easy fibre fix, add 1–2 tablespoons of chia seeds or ground flaxseed to your smoothies, oats or yoghurt every morning. I also like to enjoy two seed crackers with my lunch. Try my crackers recipe on page 188. At health-food stores, go for crackers that contain wholefoods only (e.g. gluten-free grains, nuts and seeds), and avoid those with added oils, sugar and preservatives.

## How to heal and seal your gut

These tips will help you to repair your gut. You should start to experience a change in how you feel within 3–4 weeks. Be patient. ☺

- **Pop a good multi-strain probiotic once a day, before breakfast or before going to bed, under the guidance of health practitioner.** A health practitioner can recommend a good brand and dosage for you. As a general guide, look for 50–100 billion CFU (colony forming units) and 20 strains of bacteria.
- **Enjoy fruit in the first half of the day and avoid it in the afternoons.** It triggers sugar cravings later in the evening. The best low-sugar options are berries, green apples and papaya.
- **Eat a portion of protein at each meal.** This is really important. We need the amino acids in protein to heal and seal the gut lining. Vegans need to be very conscious of this. Many struggle to get the protein they need, and then start to develop gut issues, such as leaky-gut syndrome.
- **Add a portion of good fats to each meal.** Fat helps the gut to absorb the nutrients and minerals it needs to thrive.
- **Prioritise fibre.** The goal is to include a portion of fibre in each meal. Some of my favourite high-fibre foods are dark, leafy greens (like spinach), vegetables, fruits, grains, legumes, oats, flaxseed and chia seeds.
- **Stop chewing gum.** The more you chew, the more air you're swallowing. If you're bloated all the time, gum may be to blame.
- **Avoid soft drinks (including diet varieties).** This involves the same principle as the gum: the bubbles in these drinks cause bloating. And they contain artificial ingredients that the digestive system battles to break down.
- **Drink 20 minutes before and after meals, not during.** Liquids can dilute digestive juices, making your system work harder than it needs to.
- **Add apple cider vinegar (ACV) to your water bottle and sip throughout the day.** Adding 1–2 tablespoons of ACV should do the trick. This increases stomach acid, which helps with digestion. Diluting it is better than 'shotting' it, which can be far too strong.
- **Manage your stress.** Stress has a direct impact on gut function. Serotonin (the happy hormone) is made in the gut, so if you're struggling with stress, low mood or depression, your digestion will be compromised.

**Backed up?** Try acupuncture. It's amazing for relaxing the gut and releasing tension, which can help with constipation. Magnesium citrate can also work wonders, under the guidance of a health practitioner. You can also try my JSHealth magnesium vitamins, which are available on my website.

- **Invest in a gut-healing supplement.** Probiotics aside, you may benefit from a formula that contains a mix of minerals, vitamins and herbs for gut health, like turmeric, glutamine, aloe vera and zinc. These can help to heal and seal the gut lining to reduce gut inflammation and ease constipation, diarrhoea and flatulence. Ask your nutritionist or health-food store to recommend a good brand.
- **Try giving up gluten for 2–4 weeks and note any changes in your gut health.** I've included my favourite gluten-free swaps below to make this easy!

These days, there are plenty of gluten-free alternatives readily available in supermarkets and health-food stores. These are my favourites.

## The best gluten-free swaps

| Ingredient | Replace it with ... |
|---|---|
| X Pasta | ✓ Mung bean pasta, black bean pasta, brown rice pasta, konjac noodles, zoodles (zucchini noodles) |
| X Bread | ✓ Gluten-free seed bread, brown-rice cakes, flaxseed crackers, Cauliflower and seed bread (page 124) |
| X Cereal | ✓ Organic gluten-free rolled oats, buckwheat or quinoa porridge, chia pudding, or my Cinnamon–chai coconut granola (page 74) |
| X Crackers | ✓ Brown rice cakes, Rosemary linseed crackers (page 188) |
| X White flour | ✓ Almond meal, coconut flour, oat flour, buckwheat flour |
| X Pizza | ✓ Gluten-free flaxseed pizza crust or Mini cauliflower pizza bases (page 117) |
| X Condiments with gluten | ✓ Tamari, olive oil, lemon juice, apple cider vinegar, sea salt, dijon mustard, fresh herbs and dried spices |

# 3 Cut back on caffeine

Sorry, sorry! I know you may not want to hear this one, but if you're familiar with my work, you'll know about my coffee rule: **one cup a day before 10 am.** What you may not know is that this can help you to control sugar cravings.

Caffeine has a direct impact on blood sugar levels because it increases adrenaline, which can cause a spike in our blood sugars – and then a crash later on.

From clinical experience, I've noticed that clients who drink two or more cups of coffee a day tend to have more intense sugar cravings, especially between 3 and 5 pm, and especially when they drink coffee after lunchtime. Does that sound like you?

When I ask them to reduce their caffeine intake to one cup before 10 am, their sugar cravings subside. If they're a shiftworker or a late riser, I suggest they drink that coffee sometime before 11 am. I'd like you to try doing the same. You should notice a huge difference in your energy, and in your attitude towards sugar.

Again, I'm into balance, not restriction, plus I'm a coffee lover myself, so I'll never tell you to give up your daily cup.

Often, we drink coffee during a break. It's a ritual and a time to pause. I don't want you to miss out on that, so start by working your way down. If you drink three cups a day, reduce this to two. If you're at two cups, sip on one. Then replace those extra cups with delicious caffeine alternatives, such as dandelion coffee or green juice. This way, you'll be able to satisfy your craving without having to deal with the side effects of drinking too much coffee.

# 4 Eat a protein-rich breakfast

As we discussed in Chapter 4, eating a protein-rich breakfast sets you up for a healthy day. It releases energy slowly so you can stay productive, and reduces sugar cravings as a result. On the flipside, a sugary breakfast that's high in carbs will send you on a ride on the blood sugar roller-coaster all day long. And this will trigger sugar cravings and leave you feeling less than energetic. To take control of those cravings, add good fats and fibre to your breakfast too. Please avoid these foods at breakfast:

- refined and processed boxed cereals with milk or oatmeal and honey with nothing else
- fruit on its own
- toast with jam
- yoghurt that is high in sugar. If the label says it contains more than 3–5 g of sugar per 100 g, give it a miss.
- frappuccinos with sugary syrups
- baked goods such as croissants and muffins – unless you're treating yourself, which is welcome as part of the healthy life.

## Add a portion of fat to your lunch

Not only are good fats an essential macronutrient, they also help to reduce sugar cravings. For many years, I was afraid of eating fats. (Like every fad dieter, really.) When I think back, I remember how unsatisfied I felt after not incorporating a healthy fat into my lunch, and how hungry I'd be an hour after eating.

Can you relate?

Good fats are satiating. They lift our energy and keep us feeling fuller for longer. And our bodies can easily metabolise and break down these fats when we eat them in moderation, so there's no need to be afraid of them – they are so important for your health. See the meal builder (pages 48–49) or my nutrition guide (page 238) for lists of good fats to include in your lunch. Remember to steer clear of saturated and trans fats. See page 243 for a list of fats to avoid.

## Eat balanced meals

Chapter 3 walked you through the steps of building a healthy meal and how to enjoy three meals and two snacks a day. It's so important to get familiar with these steps, especially if you want to keep your sugar consumption in check. Here's a summary.

When you start eating satiating, filling meals, your sugar cravings will decrease. Why? Because this balances your blood sugar levels – there are no gaps. There's nothing missing. You're giving your body everything it needs to function at its optimal level.

All of my meals and recipes contain all of the macronutrients. They're balanced, and carefully created with ingredients that will make you feel satisfied and energised, and keep you feeling that way.

## Manage your stress levels

When we're stressed, we're more likely to turn to sugar. I'm sure many people can relate to this. Emotionally, we crave sugar for comfort. Physiologically, high cortisol levels can trigger sugar and carb cravings – both of which send our energy plummeting even further. It's a lose-lose situation.

There are a million reasons to work on reducing your stress, and combating your sugar cravings is just one of them. Revisit Chapter 7 for my best stress-management tools and tips.

## Get 7–9 hours of sleep a night

This is easier said than done, I know. But we all know what happens when we don't get enough sleep. We're irritated, tired, moody and low on energy. And we crave sugar, and anything baked: bread, pastries, cakes, croissants …

Research confirms that a lack of sleep increases hunger. A recent study found that just one night of less or broken sleep can have an effect on our levels of leptin (the hormone that regulates appetite and fat storage) and ghrelin (the hunger hormone).

Everything's harder when you're tired.

Sugar is more appealing when you're tired.

Please, for your overall wellbeing, and to help you make healthier food choices, make sleep a priority. See Chapter 7 for my night-time routine – it's calming and really encourages good sleep. It works wonders, and it's helpful for those who struggle to fall and stay asleep.

**Top tip:** Take magnesium glycinate or citrate before bed. I call magnesium my magic mineral. It's incredible for reducing sugar cravings and promoting sleep. My JSHealth vitamins for sugar balance and metabolism should do the trick, but ask a health practitioner to point you to the right dosage.

# TESTIMONIAL

*'When my dad told me his news, I asked if he wanted to do your program together. Since that day, Dad has lost 17 kilos and I have lost 13. Neither of us started the program with the view of it being a weight-loss program; all we wanted was to achieve optimum health and a healthier maintainable lifestyle.'*

# Almond granola clusters

**DF    VEG    VEGAN**

**MAKES** 12
**PREP** 15 MINUTES +
20 MINUTES FREEZE TIME
**COOK** 5 MINUTES

———

2 tablespoons coconut oil
2 tablespoons raw cacao
    powder
2 teaspoons tahini
135 g (2 cups) Cinnamon-chai
    coconut granola (page 74)

1  Line a large baking tray with non-stick baking paper.

2  Place the oil, cacao and tahini in a small saucepan over low heat. Cook and stir for 1–2 minutes, or until the mixture has melted and is smooth. Transfer to a large heatproof bowl.

3  Add the granola and mix together until the granola is well coated in the cacao mixture. Drop heaped tablespoons of the mixture onto the prepared tray, making twelve mounds in total. Shape these into rough 7 cm rounds then place the tray in the freezer for 20 minutes, or until the clusters have set firm. Serve chilled. These will keep for up to 2 weeks in an airtight container in the fridge, or in the freezer for up to 2 months.

# Chocolate truffle protein balls

**GF    DF    VEG    VEGAN**

**MAKES** 10
**PREP** 15 MINUTES
+ 1 HOUR CHILLING

———

60 g (½ cup) chocolate protein
    powder
2 tablespoons pepitas
2 tablespoons raw cacao
1 teaspoon vanilla bean powder
70 g (¼ cup) almond butter
    or peanut butter (smooth
    or crunchy)
2 tablespoons chia seeds
80 ml (⅓ cup) warm water

1  Place all the ingredients in a small food processor. If you need to, you can add 1–2 tablespoons more warm water, to loosen the mixture a little. Process until a smooth ball forms in the bowl.

2  Roll the mixture into ten balls and place in an airtight container to refrigerate for at least 1 hour. Serve chilled and keep in the fridge for up to 2 weeks.

Almond granola clusters

Salted caramel
fro-yo

# Salted caramel fro-yo

**GF**    **VEG**

**SERVES** 1
**PREP** 5 MINUTES +
20 MINUTES FREEZE TIME

---

200 g (¾ cup) Greek yoghurt
2 tablespoons vanilla protein
    powder
½ teaspoon ground cinnamon,
    plus an extra good pinch,
    to serve
1 teaspoon tahini

1   Place all the ingredients in a serving bowl and whisk with a fork until completely smooth and well combined.

2   Place the bowl in the freezer for 20 minutes or until the mixture is just frozen. Remove and stir gently, then sprinkle with the extra cinnamon and serve immediately or store in an airtight container in the freezer for up to 1 month.

# Feta and greens frittata

**GF**    **VEG**

**SERVES** 8
**PREP** 15 MINUTES
**COOK** 25 MINUTES
+ 10 MINUTES COOLING

---

6 large eggs, whisked
1 garlic clove, crushed
3 tablespoons finely chopped
    chives
150 g Greek feta, crumbled
3 cups chopped mixed green
    vegetables (see note),
    chopped into similar-sized
    pieces
sea salt and freshly ground
    black pepper
35 g (¼ cup) slivered almonds

1   Preheat the oven to 180°C (160°C fan-forced). Line the base and sides of a 28 x 18 cm baking tin with non-stick baking paper.

2   Place the eggs, garlic and chives in a large bowl and whisk with a fork until well combined. Add the feta and vegetables and season well with salt and pepper, then mix again until well combined and all the vegetables are coated in the egg mixture.

3   Pour into the prepared tin and level it off using the back of a spoon. Sprinkle the slivered almonds on top then bake for 25 minutes, or until cooked through, golden and completely set.

4   Cool in the pan for 10 minutes, then cut into portions and serve warm, or allow to cool completely and store in an airtight container in the fridge for up to 4 days, or in the freezer for up to 2 months.

## Note

To make 3 cups of chopped veggies, try 1 bunch of asparagus, 1 medium zucchini, 1 small broccoli stalk and 2 large florets, plus 1 small kale leaf, but use whatever you have on hand.

# Carrot hummus with rosemary linseed crackers

**GF     DF     VEG     VEGAN**

**SERVES** 4
**PREP** 25 MINUTES
+ 15 MINUTES STANDING
**COOK** 45 MINUTES
+ COOLING TIME

---

**ROSEMARY LINSEED CRACKERS**

2 tablespoons chia seeds
85 g (½ cup) brown linseeds
1 tablespoon finely chopped
    fresh rosemary
½ teaspoon sea salt
125 ml (½ cup) warm water

**CARROT HUMMUS**

4 large carrots (about 650 g),
    roughly chopped
1 garlic clove, crushed
1 teaspoon ground turmeric
½ teaspoon fennel seeds
60 ml (¼ cup) tahini
zest and juice of 1 large lemon
1 tablespoon cold-pressed
    extra-virgin olive oil
sea salt and freshly ground
    black pepper

1   Preheat the oven to 160°C (140°C fan-forced). Make the rosemary linseed crackers first by combining all the ingredients in a bowl. Leave to stand for 10–15 minutes, or until the water has been absorbed. Meanwhile, line a large baking tray with non-stick baking paper.

2   Spread the cracker mixture evenly over the prepared tray in a very thin layer – about 3 mm thick. Bake for 40–45 minutes, or until crisp and golden. Leave to cool completely on the tray, then break into shards and store in an airtight container for up to 1 week.

3   While the crackers bake, place the carrots, garlic, turmeric, fennel seeds and 125 ml (½ cup) of water in a saucepan over medium heat. Stir while it comes to a simmer, then cook, stirring occasionally, for 8–10 minutes, or until the carrots are tender and the water has reduced to about 1 tablespoon. Remove the pan from the heat and stir through the tahini and the lemon zest and juice. Cool for 10 minutes.

4   Add the oil to the carrot mixture and season well with salt and pepper. Using a hand-held stick blender, purée until smooth. Spoon this mixture into a serving bowl and serve with the rosemary linseed crackers.

# Pistachio dukkah kale chips

**GF    DF    VEG    VEGAN**

**SERVES** 4
**PREP** 15 MINUTES
**COOK** 30 MINUTES

---

### KALE CHIPS

8 kale leaves, leaves torn into
   3–4 cm pieces, thick stalks
   discarded
coconut oil cooking spray

### PISTACHIO DUKKAH

30 g (¼ cup) pistachio kernels,
   toasted and very finely
   chopped
2 teaspoons ground coriander
2 teaspoons ground cumin
2 teaspoons sesame seeds
1 teaspoon fennel seeds
½ teaspoon dried mixed herbs
generous pinch of sea salt
freshly ground black pepper

1   Preheat the oven to 160°C (140°C fan-forced). Line four large baking trays with non-stick baking paper.

2   Combine all the ingredients for the pistachio dukkah in a small bowl.

3   Spread the kale evenly over the prepared trays, making sure the pieces don't overlap, then spray both sides of each piece lightly with the oil and sprinkle with pistachio dukkah.

4   Bake two trays at a time for 12–15 minutes, swapping trays halfway through cooking. Once the chips are crisp and light golden, remove from the oven and leave to cool completely on the trays. Repeat with the remaining trays.

5   Serve right away, or carefully transfer to an airtight container and store at room temperature for up to 3 days.

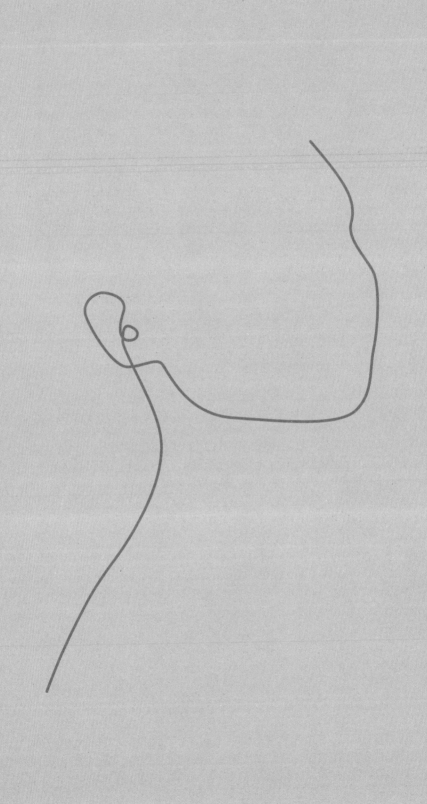

# 10

# Focus on your health, not your weight

---

*My weight controlled my life for as long as I could remember. Not anymore.*

# Overcoming 'fitspo'

These days, 'skinny' is promoted to us from all angles. The pressure to be thin and 'fit' is crazy. I feel it – do you?

Thanks to the rise of fitspo on social media, and in celebrity culture, it's hard not to feel the pressure to look a certain way. No matter how much you try to avoid it, there's a bikini model staring at you on every feed, and on every billboard. Whether we're aware of it or not, we compare ourselves to these 'perfect' models and absorb that pressure.

This is insane, especially when most people don't look like that in real life. Models are airbrushed and Photoshopped – 90 per cent of the time, the image we're seeing isn't real or realistic. What's more, many of these women endure extreme eating plans and exercise regimes. The modelling industry is known for disordered eating, and that's definitely not something to aspire to. I've met with countless models in my career, and I can tell you that it's not easy for them. It's a harsh line of work. The pressure for perfection is real, and it can have a devastating effect on their body love.

## Strive for healthy, not skinny

You are so much more than your weight, and there is so much more to life than being skinny. Your health, happiness, family, friendships and building your dream life are way more important, so channel your energy there instead.

In this chapter, we're going to focus on weight balance. By that I mean reaching your natural healthy weight – one that's easy to maintain while you live your healthy life. And this looks different for everyone.

If you've struggled with your weight your whole life, this book is here to support you. I'm going to share the strategies I've used to help people feel light again. There's never a perfect number or size or shape. Perfection doesn't exist, so we're not going to strive for it – not anymore.

You deserve to feel comfortable in your own skin, but your health really is the priority. When you're in good health, you can wake up every day feeling happy, energised and excited about life. Instead of focusing on your weight, turn your attention to your relationship with yourself and your body. That's what health is about: feeling good in your body.

If you can be grateful for and positive towards your body, you'll be on the path to freedom and true body love, for life.

When you take care of your inner health, your body naturally balances out to its ideal weight, the weight it's meant to be.

# Your body listens to your thoughts

Before we tackle how to find weight balance, I want to revisit the power of positive thinking. When it comes to achieving this, and also body love, the first place to start is in the mind. As you learned in Chapter 2, how you speak to yourself matters. A lot!

> *Dear body,*
>
> *I'm sorry for all those times I mistreated you and didn't give you the love you deserve. I haven't always spoken to you with respect and kindness. But regardless, you've stood by me, and you've been there for me no matter what. Thank you. Forgive me.*
>
> *Jess xo*

I spent so many years tangled in a negative relationship with my body, and I believe this made it harder for me to manage my weight. It certainly made it harder for me to feel good in my body and make healthy food choices. I also believe that our thoughts manifest as reality.

Calling yourself 'fat' and 'bloated' day in, day out is not going to get you closer to your weight-loss goals. We need to be gentle with ourselves.

By following all of the nutrition and lifestyle principles in this book, I'm confident you'll be able to reach your health goals. But if you're struggling to accept and respect your body (it can be so hard, I know), and recognise just how beautiful it is, I encourage you to work through these steps with love and kindness, to find peace with your body.

## Make health your focus

From now on, I want you to focus on your inner health instead of your weight, because that's what truly matters. Being healthy will mean you'll be energised, happy and light.

Health comes first. This is your new mantra.

**Weight loss is often a side effect of a** *healthy and happy body.*

## Accept your body shape as it is right now

Instead of being ashamed of your shape, celebrate it.

Your body is unique, so please stop trying to 'fix' your imperfections or comparing your body to others. It will never look exactly like the bodies on social media. To start healing, you need to stop fighting your natural body shape and show it some love. You may not love every single part of it all the time, and that's normal. All I care about is that you love it as a whole.

I've never loved my stomach, but in the last couple of years I've realised that if I had the 'best' tummy, I'd just find another body part to criticise. These days, when I catch myself criticising my stomach, I say, 'Thank you for my healthy gut and digestion.'

While I'm asking you to accept your body, I also want you to know that it's unrealistic to feel good about your body every single day. So please, remove that expectation. The goal is to feel good and confident most of the time. We all have days when we feel less comfortable in our skin, and that's okay too.

## Strive for realistic body goals

Are you uncomfortable in your own body? Be rational, kind and gentle, and carefully consider your current body size. If you still feel that you'd like to lose weight or tone up, set a realistic goal. 'Skinny' is not a healthy goal, and striving to have the same body as that model on your Instagram feed is not realistic either. But we all deserve to feel comfortable in our clothes, and the tips in this book were designed to help you to reach that place in a kind, realistic and balanced way.

Remember, you can't expect to weigh the same as you did when you were 15, 17 or 25. Our body changes as we move through life, and we need to adjust our expectations accordingly.

## The last 3–5 kilos

I've noticed so many women striving to lose 'the last 3–5 kilos'. But we never stop to consider that our bodies might be happiest where they are. Our best and most natural weight is the one that's consistent and easy to maintain. Thanks to our biological makeup, our bodies can have a set point when it comes to weight.

If you've been trying to shed a few kilos since … forever, ask yourself these questions: Are you energised? Are you comfortable in your clothes and skin? Do you feel healthy and vibrant? If so, you might have already reached your natural weight. So accept and embrace that!

The exercises on these pages are for those who genuinely believe that changing their body and losing some weight will help them to feel their absolute best. It's about the power of visualisation.

## Believe that you can achieve weight balance

You can! Your body is on your side, not against you. Say this affirmation everyday: 'I find weight balance with ease. I let go.' Write it down and stick it on your fridge or bathroom mirror so you see it every day. Do this, and you'll feel more motivated to make healthier choices. Letting go mentally helps you feel lighter physically.

## Practise gratitude

Gratitude will help you to achieve your health goals, so be grateful, not hateful! I'm a big believer in the power of gratitude. It will change your relationship with your body.

If you appreciate your body for keeping you alive and well, it will start to feel the best it ever has. So let's take the time to think about what we do have, not what we don't. I want you to wake up every day and thank your body for how hard it works to keep you alive and well. My favourite way to do this is by practising the JSHealth Body Love Scan opposite – a ritual that I developed (and thousands of people use) to flood the body with gratitude and love.

## Harness the power of the mind

If you're hoping to find weight balance, wake up each day and picture yourself looking and feeling your best. Get excited to become that person. It's happening right now. Just surrender, be kind to yourself, appreciate your body as it is now, and focus on eating and exercising with balance. Try this manifesting exercise.

1   Get a piece of paper and write down exactly how you'd like to feel in your body. You might write: 'I want to feel light in my body. I want to feel energised in my body. I want to feel healthy in my body. I want to feel confident in my body and in my clothes.' Use any words that uplift you and make you feel inspired.
2   Stick this piece of paper on your mirror, next to your bed or somewhere you'll see it every day.
3   Read the list out loud every day, and imagine that you already feel that way. I truly believe that our thoughts create our reality. This is a powerful manifestation exercise that will help you not only to reach a balanced weight, but also to appreciate your body and feel grateful for it.

# \* *Activity*
# THE JSHEALTH
# BODY LOVE SCAN

Every morning, I spend 2 minutes imagining waves of love and positive energy pouring into each part of my body from head to toe.

Join me in doing this first thing in the morning, while you're still lying in bed. It's designed to boost self-love and help you to reconnect with your beautiful body. You may need to adapt some of the points depending on your own health and circumstances, but remember to focus on the things you're grateful for.

1  Close your eyes and take three deep breaths. Imagine good energy and love going through each body part.

2  Starting with your head, say the following affirmation: 'Thank you for my clear mind and for my healthy brain function.'

3  Move your focus to your thyroid gland, which is in the middle of your throat. Here, say to yourself, 'Thank you for my healthy, functioning thyroid gland, which provides me with my healthy metabolism so I have the energy to do what I love every day.'

4  Next, imagine the love and good energy moving to your digestive system. Here, say, 'I love myself enough to let go of the negativity, and treat myself with the love and care I deserve.'

5  Then, focus on your reproductive organs. Say, 'Thank you for my healthy reproductive organs, menstrual cycle and hormonal balance.'

6  Now, I want you to thank your legs and feet: 'Thank you for allowing me to walk through life, and for keeping me grounded.'

7  Imagine all of that love flowing through your entire body. Breathe it all in. Your body is so grateful for this love.

8  Take three deep breaths, and slowly open your eyes.

## Forgive yourself, and others

As I've said before, it's not your fault if you've developed an unhealthy relationship with food or your body, so please don't blame yourself. Forgive yourself for your thoughts, and feel that relief. Let it go!

And while you're at it, try to identify any grudges and negative experiences you may be holding on to. Emotional heaviness can cause physical heaviness, so forgiving that person or situation is going to help you heal – it's so freeing. They're not worth the time and energy you're giving to them. I've learned that lesson.

Whenever those grudges and feelings of blame pop up, it helps to say out loud, 'I let go.' This will encourage your body to release the heaviness. Personally, I love saying this at the gym or before heading into a yoga class.

## Know that you're going to be okay

Sometimes, we hold on to weight to protect us when we don't feel a sense of safety and security in our lives.

Is there anything in your life that's making you feel unsafe? Your relationship? Money? A person you work with? It's important to address these feelings of uncertainty. (Therapy can seriously help.)

Say this affirmation out loud: 'I am safe.' Say it as much as you need to, and feel the relief.

## Eat with balance

As we discussed at the very start of this book, diets make our weight much harder to control in the long term. When your body is in 'starvation mode' from restricting food, it tries to protect you by holding on to fat. When you respect your body, you naturally make better, healthier choices.

All of the recipes in this book are nutritionally balanced to support your blood sugar levels, decrease cravings and increase energy. Since they're nutritionally dense, you won't feel the need to eat as much. And all of these things play a role in helping you to find your ideal weight.

Finally, give yourself permission to indulge. Do that, and you won't feel the need to binge or overeat on 'forbidden' foods. Remember, our body responds to what we do the majority of the time. It can handle all foods in small amounts. (More on this in the next chapter.)

## Are you overeating?

If the answer is yes, the reasons may surprise you!
Overeating can be traced back to several factors:

- You're not eating enough at each meal.
- You're not adding protein and fat to your meals. Protein and fat are important macronutrients, and they keep us feeling full and satisfied.
- Your breakfast isn't supporting your blood sugar and energy levels.
- You're still stuck in a diet mentality of restriction.
- You're not sleeping enough.
- Your cortisol levels are too high.
- You drink multiple cups of coffee a day. This can increase anxiety, impact sleep and send your stress levels soaring, all of which can affect your weight.
- You're not eating mindfully.
- You're exercising too much, or too intensely.
- You eat while scrolling through your phone. Now, more than ever, it's so important to separate yourself from technology at mealtimes.
- You grew up in a household where you were forced to finish everything on your plate. It's time to let that go.
- Emotionally, you feel empty. Please know that you don't have to deal with these feelings alone.

## Exercise kindly and moderately

I encourage you to move your body daily in ways you love – without overdoing it. For weight loss, it's important to build lean muscle through strength training, and things like yoga and Pilates, combined with short bursts of cardio, such as HIIT on the treadmill (see my Body Blitz workout on page 59) or brisk walking. It revs up the metabolism for several hours after you finish exercising – meaning your body is still burning calories while it recovers.

A study of young women found that participants following 'acute resistance exercise' experienced 'prolonged elevations of post-exercise metabolic rate.' Their resting metabolic rate increased by 4.2 per cent, which is pretty significant!

Tens of thousands of women on the JSHealth program have effectively reached their health goals by exercising moderately with kindness, not insanely.

## Know that you're worthy of feeling good about yourself

You're too precious to let food or ridiculous body standards define you. Focus on being the best version of yourself. Repeat after me: 'I am enough. My body is unique. I refuse to compare my beautiful body to someone else's.'

The comparing has to stop for the sake of healing – and your sanity.

## Release the pressure you're feeling

I've spoken about this before, but a little positive reinforcement can't hurt! Some of us are experts at putting pressure on ourselves to be perfect. This adds an enormous amount of stress and anxiety to the body, and can lead to body dissatisfaction, bingeing, emotional eating and, in turn, weight gain. Truly.

See Chapter 7 for a reminder on ways to relieve the pressure.

## Manage your stress levels

Are you stressed? Being constantly stressed can increase emotional eating, bingeing and stress eating – all of which make weight loss much more challenging.

For weight balance specifically, I tell my clients to focus on connecting to their breath. I recommend doing ten to twenty deep belly breaths when you wake up, and then again before bed. I do this every day. I also encourage them to take three deep, long breaths before eating.

Yoga is another brilliant way to connect to your breath.

## Create your own definition of beautiful

What does beautiful mean to you?

For me, it means waking up with energy to do what I love, feeling confident in my skin, accepting my imperfections with kindness and eating to feel GOOD. It's about fitting comfortably in my clothes.

It's so easy to succumb to social media and the Hollywood ideal and believe that that's what we need to look like to be 'healthy'. Remember, most of the time, those bodies are Photoshopped, airbrushed and starved – and that's the furthest thing from healthy.

So what's your definition of beautiful? Make it your own.

# Combatting negative body image

Body image refers to the way you view your own physical appearance – how you picture yourself in your mind, how you feel about your body and how you judge the way you look. Sometimes, when women are struggling with their weight or body issues, their body image is negative or skewed to a point where it's not a true reflection of them at all. (This is called body dysmorphia.)

Battling a negative body image can be really tough if you're trying to make changes and live a healthy life, because, as we learned in Chapter 2, the key to a healthy life is having a healthy mindset.

Do you suffer from a negative body image?

If the answer isn't immediately obvious, ask yourself the following questions:

- Does your outer appearance dictate how much you love yourself?
- Do you focus on your body's flaws or imperfections more than the parts you love?
- Do you avoid going to certain places (e.g. the beach or a party) because you feel insecure about your appearance?
- Do you feel anxious or worried about how others are judging your body all the time?
- Do you find yourself checking the mirror on a regular basis and feeling unhappy with what you see?
- Do you wish you had a different body shape?
- Do you constantly compare your body to others?
- Do you find yourself latching on to fad diets in the hope they will change how you look?

If you found yourself relating to many of those questions, there's a good chance your body image needs a boost. You don't have to manage this alone. This book will help you learn to love and appreciate your body – and this will automatically steer you towards a positive body image. However, I highly recommend seeing a therapist for support if you're struggling with negative thoughts. A good therapist can help you to let go of beliefs that have trapped you, and the pressure you're holding on to. Therapy worked wonders for me, and I credit it with speeding up my healing, though it's still a journey. Don't be afraid to ask for help.

## Photos mean nothing
It's okay if not every photo of you is flattering. Lighting, angles and clothing all play a part in pictures. Don't judge your appearance based on photos, and please don't let a less-than-flattering photo consume your thoughts all day or week.

# Negative body image is an ongoing battle

While writing this book, I struggled with negative body image. In fact, I've noticed that negative feelings about my body seem to pop up every time I write a book. But I'm grateful they do, as this allows me to connect with my readers in a very real and vulnerable way. I've been doing tons of TV appearances and photoshoots lately, and these have always made me feel self-conscious and triggered my body-image issues. I'm only human! I'm not immune to my negative thoughts, but at least I have the tools to manage them, so I treat myself with care and kindness and I know they'll pass. It's normal to have days when we criticise ourselves more.

This is incredible progress for me. In my early twenties, self-inflicted negativity like this would have consumed my thoughts for an entire day or week. Remember the story I told of being a child in my bikini and hearing that my (non-existent) tummy was 'fat'? Because of that, being in a bikini can still be difficult for me. Until my early twenties, I spent hours staring at myself in the mirror and criticising certain body parts I thought should be thinner or more toned. Then I'd find photos of myself and criticise those too.

When we suffer from negative body image, we tend to focus on the body parts we don't like. This is when body dysmorphia kicks in. I'm sad that I spent most of my life body hating rather than body loving. As a young girl, I wish I'd had someone guiding me and reminding me to stop striving for perfection. To tell me that what I was born with is beautiful, that it's enough, and that perfection isn't the goal.

Don't let your poor body image ruin another holiday, experience or event. This book will help you to relieve the pressure and make peace with your body.

## Real talk …

When I'm dealing with negative body image, I find I crave approval – I just need someone to compliment me on my body so I can feel at peace. I'll ask Dean, 'Do I look like I've put on weight?' The anxiety is so consuming, that I can't help it. Do you ever feel the same? Unfortunately, this tactic is more damaging than helpful. People never say exactly what we want them to, and even if they did, their words can't solve the deep-rooted issues of negative body image. Only YOU can do that.

# Let's work on this together

Many of the daily practices I've shared so far work wonders for me in terms of staying balanced and warding off negative thoughts. These practices include setting social media boundaries, getting enough sleep, taking steps to manage my stress, and prioritising self-care. Each of these things really helps me to maintain a healthy and positive mindset.

For long-term healing, I see a therapist on and off, and I also use all the tools we've talked about in this chapter to nourish my relationship with myself. This keeps my self-esteem and body image in check.

But, inevitably, our thoughts run away from us and we experience waves of negative thinking. The list below is what I (affectionately) refer to as my Body-Image Emergency Toolkit. It includes the exact strategies I use to get me through any negative body-image moments. Now it's yours to use too!

---

*\* Activity*

## THE BODY-IMAGE EMERGENCY TOOLKIT

– I steer clear of my triggers. For me, that means photos of myself, as well as scales, social media and researching diet trends. All of these things can trigger negative thoughts, so when I'm feeling vulnerable, I go out of my way to avoid them. I delete social media until I'm feeling less vulnerable.

– I go outside (nature is so grounding) and listen to music. It really calms me down.

– I don't let myself sit with the thoughts, as that usually makes them worse. I try to get out of my head by doing something such as yoga, going for a walk or chatting to a friend.

– I say positive affirmations to myself all day (even if they don't feel real). For example, I repeat the following: 'Thank you for my health. Thank you for my legs that carry me around. Thank you for my clear mind. Thank you for my fulfilling work and incredible family.' Gratitude eases the anxiety.

– I speak to myself with kindness – even more than usual. This is one of the most valuable strategies in my toolkit. Instead of judging myself for struggling with body image, I just have a kind conversation with myself. I accept the thoughts, and I let them come and go. I say, 'Jess, this will pass.' I find this calms the mental chatter.

– I do the JSHealth Mirror Exercise. Do you think something negative or critical about yourself every time you look in a mirror? The self-doubt ends now! You are enough. From now on, never pass a mirror without giving yourself a compliment. The next time you catch yourself looking at a mirror and saying, 'OMG, my stomach looks bloated,' or 'My butt is too big,' go back and find a part of your body you feel grateful for (it can be anything!), and offer yourself a compliment.

– I remind myself that I'm not alone.

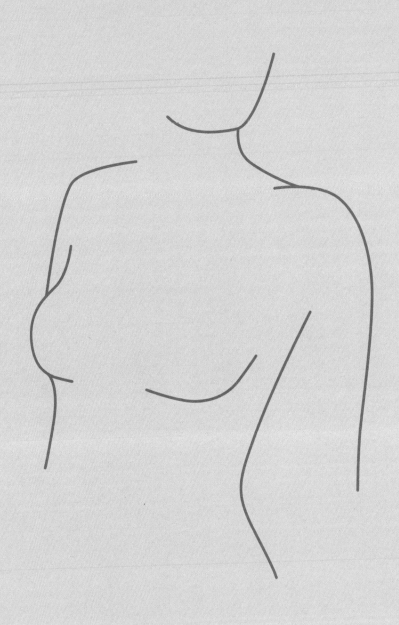

# 11

# Indulge moderately, without guilt!

---

*Moderation is my mantra. If I don't allow myself to indulge, I'm tempted to binge – this approach helps keeps my healthy eating on track.*

# I used to be scared of indulging

In the past, I'd rarely allow myself treats because the thought of deviating from my diet was petrifying. I was striving to be skinny, so I saw treats as 'evil'. And when I did indulge, I'd be consumed by guilt that would last for days or even weeks.

I deprived myself of all my favourite indulgent foods. I thought they'd make me gain weight in a matter of minutes. (Crazy, but true!) And I didn't trust my body, even though I now know that it was always there for me.

My self-imposed ban on treats led me to dream about things like hazelnut gelato, and fantasising about food isn't healthy. You can probably guess what happened next ... After a short period of time, my mind and body would rebel. They couldn't handle the deprivation and pressure anymore, so I'd end up bingeing or overeating those foods I'd been missing. Of course, this would send me into a spiral of self-loathing, guilt and punishment – and my go-to methods of punishment were 2 hours of spin class and cutting my daily calories even more. It was a torturous cycle.

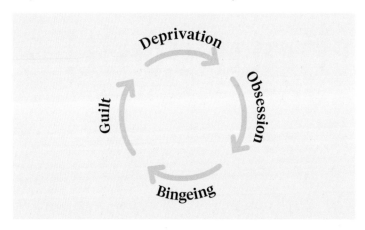

But when you tell yourself you can't have a certain food, it haunts you until you crack.

These days, I approach indulging VERY differently. Now that I've repaired my relationship with food (and myself), I love to indulge. In fact, I make sure I do – and I've never felt better. I now see that indulging in moderation is not only healthy, it's also good for the mind, body and soul. So I go out of my way to diverge from my usual clean-eating routine a couple of times a week. That's balance.

The key to *healthy* indulgence is *moderation* and *mindfulness*. I eat everything I *love* in small amounts, and with *joy* – and *no guilt*

When I started giving myself permission to indulge (with creamy gelato, red wine and pasta), I stopped bingeing and overeating. There was no need to stuff myself until I was uncomfortable because I knew my next treat was coming later that week. My mind relaxed. Suddenly, I could control my portion sizes. Suddenly, I had no problem making healthy food choices most of the time out of self-love, not self-inflicted punishment. When I relaxed and quit the cycle of restriction and bingeing, my weight balanced out too.

# What does it mean to indulge in moderation?

Do you find it hard to have two or three pieces of chocolate (rather than the whole block) or stop at one slice of cake? If your answer is yes, I get it!

The nutritionist in me says this is probably because you're telling yourself you 'can't' or 'shouldn't' eat that food. Whether it's mild or severe, this deprivation mentality often leads us to overeat indulgent foods. We eat as if the food is running away from us and we'll never have access to it again. We go nuts on the food in front of us because we've convinced ourselves that we'll be 'better tomorrow' or that the 'diet starts on Monday'.

We binge because of a pressure to be perfect the next day, or the next week. This is another reason diets almost always fail.

From what I've witnessed, people who can have two or three pieces of chocolate seem to have a healthier relationship with food. They don't believe they have to make up for a treat by eating perfectly the next day or following a radical diet. They savour the treat, and then forget about it – knowing they can always have more anther time. This is a more balanced approach to food. Perhaps I'm generalising here, but that's truly what I've observed – both in my clients and members of the JSHealth community.

Indulgence is part of living a healthy, balanced life. Embracing it rather than resisting it will bring a sense of balance and satisfaction to your life.

# Treat yourself, minus the guilt

It's time to reset your mindset and embrace indulgence in moderation.

As I said, I indulge two or three times a week. This keeps my healthy eating on track, and I no longer have intense cravings or fantasise about any 'forbidden' foods because nothing is forbidden. It's an amazing feeling!

I want you to try doing the same. You'll find that this approach will help you to sustain and maintain your healthy life in the long term. Why? Because you'll never feel deprived.

THE 12-STEP MIND-BODY-FOOD RESET

Guess what? It's okay to get popcorn when you go to the movies. It's okay to sip on a glass of red wine on the weekend. And it's okay to order dessert when you're celebrating.

Your clothes will still fit comfortably after an indulgent meal or two. Please, don't worry. Weight gain usually only occurs if you indulge daily or binge on foods you've been denying yourself.

P.S. If you're still craving sugar, flick back to Chapter 9 for my tips and tricks to help you bust those cravings.

# HERE'S YOUR PLAN OF ACTION

1   Choose a treat that you truly feel like eating, in a moderate portion size. Tune in to your body and think, 'Balance'.
2   Sit down to eat it.
3   Savour every single mouthful. Chew and enjoy your food.
4   During or after eating, say positive affirmations such as, 'My body knows how to digest and metabolise this.' 'I trust my body.' 'I eat with joy.' This is so calming for the mind.
5   Remind yourself that you can eat more later or tomorrow. Say this out loud, if you can. It'll slow you right down.
6   Trust your beautiful body to do its job and break down the food. It's here to support you.
7   Move on with your day. Avoid thinking about your indulgence.

## Give yourself permission to indulge

I suggest choosing two or three indulgent meals or snacks a week, and then sitting down to eat them mindfully and with joy – not guilt.

Think of your top picks in advance and look forward to them. I find that when people are working on healing their relationship with food, planning indulgences can alleviate any stress associated with treating themselves.

I love having an indulgent meal on a Saturday night that includes wine, pasta and a dessert, such as gelato. As you may have seen on my Instagram, I adore going to Italian restaurants! I also enjoy a delicious treat during the week, such as a scone for breakfast or a glass of wine with dinner. After indulging, I feel so free and proud that I was able to indulge in moderation. I also feel excited to get back to my healthy eating the next meal, or day. It's a balanced way to live. So much peace, so little stress. How divine does that sound?

## Your tastebuds are going to change

When we start to embrace the healthy life, our tastebuds adapt, and we begin craving healthier foods that don't contain refined sugar. You'll find you feel so much better after eating the healthier options (say goodbye to bloating and blood sugar crashes!).

To be honest, these days I crave banana nice-cream, healthy brownies and bliss balls more than the not-so-healthy treats! But absolutely, give yourself permission to treat yourself to the 'unhealthier' versions of foods too. Enjoy everything in moderation. Your body can handle it.

There are some seriously good, wholesome sweet treats at the end of this chapter and you'll also find some great snack ideas on pages 176–77.

# The lowdown on emotional eating and bingeing

Emotional eating and bingeing starts to subside when we free ourselves from diets and extremes, and begin to eat intuitively. But to reach that place, we first need to understand the emotional reasons driving our behaviour.

**Emotional eating** tends to occur as a result of stress, anger, pressure, a deprivation mentality, loneliness, boredom and even happiness. We use food to feed our feelings, or fill the gap if something's missing in our life. From a holistic point of view, ask yourself these questions: How am I feeling? Are there any emotions that I've been pushing down and bottling up? Is there a part of my life I feel I need to manage a little better?

As always, awareness is the first step.

For me, migrating to a new country as a teenager shattered my self-esteem. I was dealing with the turbulent emotions that come with puberty, and the teething issues that come with living in an unfamiliar place. I turned to dieting and emotional eating for comfort and confidence, but I only uncovered the root cause of my disordered eating patterns once I went to therapy. My therapist helped me to find other tools to deal with the pain I felt about leaving my birth country. I recommend seeing a therapist, so they can guide you and you don't have to feel alone.

**Bingeing**, like emotional eating, can be linked to stress, anger, pressure, happiness, dieting, deprivation and distraction. In my experience, it's usually the result of having a complicated relationship with food, adopting a diet mentality and succumbing to pressure, as well as a general feeling of not being good enough.

People also tend to binge when they feel like there may not be 'enough' food. This could be due to dieting for a long time, or their home environment. Say, for example, if the cook of the household doesn't make enough food, or if siblings are always stealing food from each other's plates. As we know, when we deprive ourselves of food, we develop fear around food – which can lead to a need to overeat.

Often, we fall into a pattern of bingeing without even realising what's happening. It's part of the diet culture, and I believe it has become an epidemic. While many people joke about it, bingeing can be a truly scary experience.

Those who binge know that food takes over. When I binged, I truly felt like I had no control. And I'm a person who is usually very 'in control'. For women especially, the way we beat ourselves up after a binge or overeating spree is worse for our health than any bad food.

You are too precious for this.

# How to transition from emotional eating or bingeing

If you're struggling with these issues, you're not alone. I'm here supporting you. We're in this together. These tips will help you to find balance again.

1   **Quit dieting, restriction and deprivation.** Bingeing or emotional eating is often a subconscious rebellion against the deprivation of dieting. To free yourself from this vicious cycle, you'll need to give up diets for good. Instead of denying your body of food, nourish it with wholefoods. It's important to treat your body with love. Do this, and you'll naturally make healthier choices.

2   **Give yourself permission to eat with joy.** Don't cloud your eating experiences with negative thoughts. Too many people view food as 'good' or 'bad', and this creates stress and can increase emotional eating. Become a mindful eater who eats with joy, not guilt. So sit down, eat slowly and enjoy the eating experience. At mealtimes, connect to your mind by expressing gratitude. Say something like, 'Thank you for the food in front of me. I know it's going to nourish my body and give it the nutrients it needs.'

3   **Tune in to your appetite.** The next time you're hungry, ask yourself what you really need? Tuning in to your body takes practice, but you'll be surprised by how wise your inner voice really is. Maybe you just need water, a rest or a walk outside in the fresh air. When you're truly hungry, allow yourself to eat (without guilt), and respect your body when you're not hungry.

4   **Commit to eating wholefoods that support your body.** When you start eating meals that satisfy you and support your body's

systems, you'll eat less and be less inclined to eat emotionally. See Chapter 3 for my guide to creating wholesome meals.

**5** **Plan your meals ahead of time and snack wisely in between.** Structure is really helpful for emotional and binge eaters. Aim to enjoy three meals and two snacks a day to keep your blood sugar levels in check. See Chapter 9 for my go-to snacks and Chapter 3 for how to build a well-balanced, satiating meal.

**6** **Watch your stress levels.** We know that stress can lead to emotional eating and bingeing. Please re-read Chapter 7 to learn how to manage stress effectively. When you're stressed, try to nurture yourself in other ways besides food. Soak in a bath, get a mani, hit a yoga class, plan a trip or read a book.

**7** **Show yourself love in ways that aren't centred around food.** This tip is in the same vein as the one above, but it's important to make time for yourself every day, not just when you're stressed out. So each day, do just one thing that makes you feel calm. For me, that's having a bath with lavender oil, watching feel-good TV, walking in nature or meditating. I'm so committed to this. While you're at it, release the need to criticise yourself, and know that you are doing your best. You are doing enough.

**8** **Let go of what you ate yesterday or on the weekend.** Today is a new day. Trust that your body can break down any imperfect food you perhaps overindulged in. Your body has your back!

**9** **Sleep longer.** When we're tired, food becomes more comforting, and sugary and salty foods are much more appealing. Fatigue can trigger overeating, emotional eating or unhealthy food choices, so for the sake of your health, aim to get between 7 and 9 hours of sleep a night. In Chapter 7, you'll find a beautiful night-time routine to help you fall (and stay) asleep.

**10** **Ask for support.** Sometimes we don't want to admit we have a problem because we're scared we'll disappoint family or friends. But there's nothing to be ashamed of if you're experiencing disordered eating. Please enlist the help of a nutritionist, integrative doctor or therapist for support.

**11** **Whip up healthier versions of your favourite treats.** Do you find that you can easily crush an entire block of chocolate, yet battle to eat a batch of cacao brownies? That's because the brownies are nutrient-dense and contain ingredients that make you feel fuller. Give yourself permission to indulge on whatever you desire. But I encourage you to make healthier versions of treats you love. They're more nutritious and harder to binge on.

**12** **Don't eat as soon as you get home.** Binges often happen when people get home from work. The pressures of the day hit them and they turn to food for comfort. When you walk through the door, give yourself half an hour to shower, take ten deep breaths, put your phone away and change into comfy clothes. Only enter the kitchen when you feel calm and centred. Then, tune in to what you feel like eating and enjoy it mindfully.

**13** **Don't eat while standing** – whether that's at the kitchen counter, in front of the fridge or walking around the house. Sitting down to your meals is part of eating mindfully.

**14** **Look at Sunday as a day of self-care.** Sunday can be a big binge day for people who feel anxious about the week ahead. If you suffer from the Sunday blues, use this day to nourish yourself in other ways. Rest, watch movies, get a massage or spend an hour prepping meals for the week ahead (see Chapter 6). Catch up with friends and family if you're up for it, and say no to social arrangements if you're not. Be sure to go to bed early that night.

**15** **Don't put pressure on yourself to follow the 'perfect' eating plan.** When it comes to eating, we already know that pressure usually backfires in the long term. Instead, commit to balance and eating in a way that nourishes your mind, body and soul.

## Healthier swaps for some of your favourite treats

These healthier alternatives really hit the spot. In saying this, please still give yourself permission to enjoy the real thing too!

Pizza ⟹ Cauliflower pizza with pesto, broccoli and parmesan (see page 117)
Pasta ⟹ Zoodles with a creamy Napoletana sauce (see page 122)
Chocolate ⟹ Chocolate truffle protein balls (page 184)
Hot chocolate ⟹ Warm almond milk with cacao, cinnamon and stevia or honey
Brownies ⟹ Chocolate cake with choc-coconut frosting (page 220)
Gelato ⟹ Salted caramel fro-yo (page 187)
Popcorn ⟹ Natural popcorn without added sugar or preservatives
Cheesecake ⟹ Vegan lemon and blueberry cheesecake (page 226)
White wine ⟹ Organic red wine
Cocktails ⟹ Gin/vodka/tequila with fresh lemon, lime, cucumber slices and soda
Cookies ⟹ Choc-chunk blondies with coconut cookie dough crumble (page 224)
Chips and dips ⟹ Kale chips (see page 190) and hummus

# Baked pumpkin pie doughnuts

**GF** **DF** **VEG**

**MAKES** 10
**PREP** 15 MINUTES
**COOK** 20 MINUTES
+ 5 MINUTES COOLING

---

coconut oil cooking spray
250 g (1 cup) cooled, puréed
    steamed pumpkin (see note)
2 large eggs, whisked
80 ml (⅓ cup) rice malt syrup
2 tablespoons cold-pressed
    extra-virgin olive oil
1 teaspoon vanilla bean powder
225 g (2¼ cups) almond meal
1 tablespoon chia seeds
1 teaspoon baking powder

**SPICED SUGAR**
120 g (¾ cup) coconut sugar
2 teaspoons ground cinnamon
1 teaspoon mixed spice

## Note

You will need a kent pumpkin approximately 500 g for this recipe. To prepare it, peel, remove the seeds, then roughly chop the flesh. Steam the pumpkin over a large saucepan of boiling water for 10–15 minutes, or until the pumpkin is tender and a knife passes through the largest chunks easily. Remove from the heat and allow the pumpkin to cool before blitzing in a food processor until smooth.

1 Preheat the oven to 180°C (160°C fan-forced). Prepare two 6-hole, ⅓-cup capacity doughnut trays by spraying ten holes liberally with the cooking oil.

2 Combine all of the spiced sugar ingredients in a large heatproof bowl then set aside.

3 Whisk the wet doughnut ingredients together, then add the dry ingredients and stir until well combined and smooth.

4 Using a teaspoon, carefully spoon ¼-cup measures of the batter into the prepared doughnut holes.

5 Bake for 18–20 minutes, swapping the trays halfway through cooking. The doughnuts are cooked when they are golden and firm to the touch. Remove the trays from the oven and allow to stand for 5 minutes (don't leave the doughnuts in the trays any longer than this or they'll be hard to remove).

6 Using a small soft spatula, carefully release each doughnut from its hole, then turn the trays over to gently tap them out onto a wire rack. These doughnuts are very soft, so it's very important to allow them to rest in the doughnut tray for a few minutes before removing them, as they'll fall apart if you take them out too soon.

7 Roll each doughnut in the spiced sugar mixture while warm to coat well on all sides, then eat right away. These are best eaten on the day they are made, and you may need to re-roll them in the spiced sugar if they are left for a while before serving.

# Carrot cake slice with vanilla cashew cream

**GF** **DF** **VEG**

**MAKES** 16 SLICES
**PREP** 30 MINUTES
+ OVERNIGHT SOAKING
+ 1 HOUR CHILLING
**COOK** 20 MINUTES
+ COOLING TIME

---

3 large eggs, whisked
2 carrots (about 250 g),
    coarsely grated
180 ml (¾ cup) cold-pressed
    extra-virgin olive oil
80 g (½ cup) coconut sugar
100 g (1 cup) almond meal
65 g (½ cup) arrowroot flour
1 teaspoon vanilla bean powder
1 teaspoon baking powder
1 teaspoon ground cinnamon
65 g (½ cup) finely chopped
    walnuts, plus extra to serve
flaked coconut, to serve
thin strips of lemon zest,
    to serve

**VANILLA CASHEW
CREAM**
155 g (1 cup) raw cashews,
    soaked overnight in water,
    drained well
1 teaspoon vanilla bean powder
1 tablespoon pure maple syrup
60 g (¼ cup) coconut cream
zest of ½ lemon

1    Start by making the cashew cream. Add the drained cashew nuts to a high-speed blender with the rest of the vanilla cashew cream ingredients. Blend for 1 minute, or until the mixture is completely smooth. Depending on the thickness of your coconut cream you may also need to add 1–2 tablespoons of water. Once ready, set aside until ready to serve.

2    Preheat the oven to 180°C (160°C fan-forced). Line a 26 x 18 cm baking tin with non-stick baking paper.

3    Using a fork, whisk the eggs, carrot and oil together in a large bowl until well combined. Fold in the remaining cake ingredients. Spread the mixture evenly over the base of the prepared tin.

4    Bake for 18–20 minutes, or until the cake is cooked and golden. You can test for doneness by inserting a skewer into the centre of the cake. If it comes out clean, it's ready. Remove from the oven and allow the cake to cool completely in the tin. Once cooled, spread the vanilla cashew cream evenly over the top and refrigerate for at least 1 hour before serving.

5    Sprinkle the top of the chilled slice with the flaked coconut, extra walnuts and strips of lemon zest.

## Note

This slice freezes really well. If you want to do this, you can either wrap the whole slice while still in the tin (after it has cooled completely) or wrap individual portions of the slice after they've been chilled (this firms up the vanilla cashew cream), and freeze for up to 2 months. To defrost, leave the slice at room temperature for 30 minutes and serve while still firm and chilled, or leave to defrost in the fridge overnight.

*Indulge moderately, without guilt!*

# Chocolate cake with choc-coconut frosting

**GF**   **DF**   **VEG**

**SERVES** 8–10
**PREP** 35 MINUTES
**COOK** 35 MINUTES
+ COOLING TIME

——

125 ml (½ cup) melted coconut
    oil
120 g (¾ cup) coconut sugar
40 g (⅓ cup) raw cacao powder
2 large eggs
100 g (1 cup) almond meal
65 g (½ cup) arrowroot flour
2 teaspoons baking powder
1 tablespoon apple cider vinegar
fresh figs, raspberries,
    strawberries and
    blueberries, to serve
cacao nibs, to serve

**RASPBERRY SPREAD**
125 g (1 cup) fresh raspberries
2 teaspoons pure maple syrup

**CHOC-COCONUT
FROSTING**
400 g tin coconut cream,
    refrigerated upside down
    for at least 48 hours
1 teaspoon vanilla bean powder
1 tablespoon pure maple syrup
2 teaspoons raw cacao

1   Preheat the oven to 180°C (160°C fan-forced). Line the base and side of a 20 cm round cake tin with non-stick baking paper.

2   Place all the cake ingredients in a large bowl and stir until well combined and smooth. Spoon the mixture into the prepared tin and level the surface using the back of a spoon or a palette knife.

3   Bake for 30–35 minutes, or until the cake has set firmly in the centre and is light golden. Insert a skewer into the middle of the cake, if it comes out clean, it's ready. Allow the cake to cool completely in the tin. Once cooled, remove from the tin.

4   Make the raspberry spread while the cake cools. Use a fork to crush the raspberries and syrup together in a bowl, then chill until required.

5   Make the choc-coconut frosting by opening the can of chilled coconut cream and using a dessert spoon to scoop out the firmly set cream that has separated and is sitting at the top of the tin (you should get about ¾ cup). Save the coconut water (see notes).

6   When you're ready to assemble the cake, place the chilled coconut cream in a large chilled bowl. Using a balloon whisk, whisk the cream gently until it comes together and has a smooth consistency. Add the vanilla, syrup and half the cacao, and whisk again well combined, light and fluffy.

7   To assemble, place the cake on a serving plate. Spoon the choc-coconut frosting on top of the cake and spread it around evenly. Spoon the raspberry spread over the choc-coconut frosting and spread it around evenly. Finish the cake off with some figs and berries, and dust lightly with the remaining cacao.
Serve immediately (see notes).

## Notes

Pour the leftover coconut water from the chilled coconut cream into an airtight container and use it in smoothies or baking in place of your milk of choice.

The cake can be made a day ahead of serving and kept in the fridge overnight. But once the cake is decorated it's best to serve it straight away.

# Choc-fudge granola squares

**DF    VEG    VEGAN**

**MAKES** 12 SQUARES
**PREP** 25 MINUTES
+ 30 MINUTES FREEZE
**COOK** 5 MINUTES

———

270 g (4 cups) Cinnamon-chai
    coconut granola (page 74)
125 ml (½ cup) melted
    coconut oil

**CHOC-FUDGE FILLING**
100 g (½ cup) cacao butter
    buttons (see notes)
80 g (¾ cup) raw cacao powder
125 ml (½ cup) pure maple syrup
2 teaspoons ground cinnamon

1   Line the base and sides of a 20 cm square cake tin with non-stick baking paper.

2   Crumble half the granola into a bowl and add half the coconut oil. Stir together until well combined, then spread this mixture evenly over the base of the prepared tin, pressing down firmly as you go. Freeze for 20 minutes, or until the granola base has set firm.

3   Make the choc-fudge filling by melting the cacao butter buttons in a small saucepan over medium heat. Transfer to a bowl, immediately add the remaining ingredients and whisk together until well combined, smooth and thick. Immediately spread the choc-fudge evenly over the firmly set granola.

4   Mix the remaining crumbled granola with the remaining oil until well combined, then scatter evenly over the choc-fudge filling. Return to the freezer for 10 minutes, or until almost set firm. Cut into 12 squares and serve chilled (see notes).

## Note

Cacao buttons can be found in health-food stores, or ordered online.

Once sliced and stored in an airtight container, these will keep in the fridge for up to 1 week and in the freezer for up to 2 months.

*Indulge moderately, without guilt!*

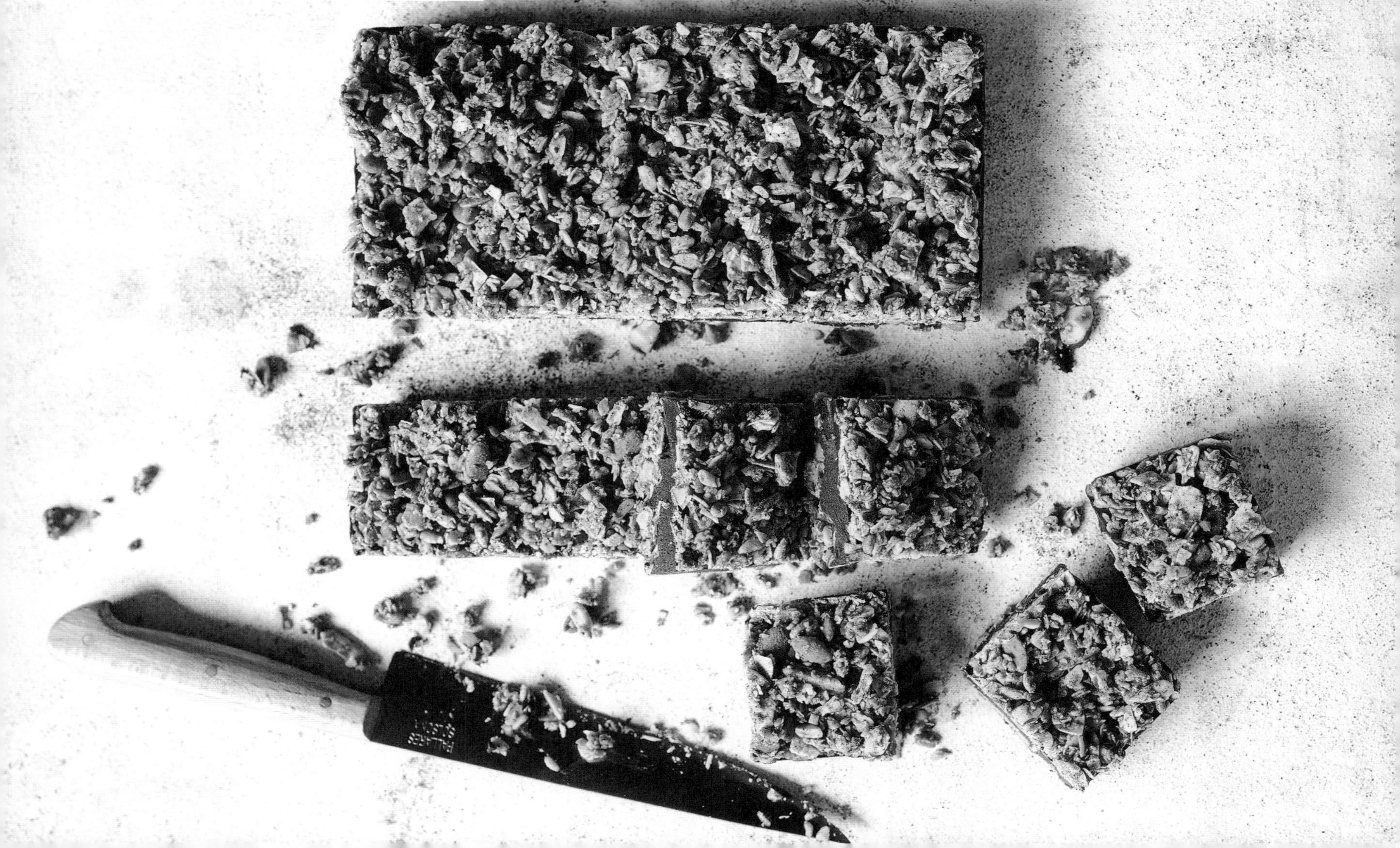

# Choc-chunk blondies with coconut cookie dough crumble

**GF    DF    VEG**

**MAKES** 16–20 BLONDIES
**PREP** 25 MINUTES
**COOK** 30 MINUTES
+ COOLING TIME

———

100 g (½ cup) cacao butter
    buttons (see note on page
    222), melted and cooled
200 g (2 cups) almond meal
1 tablespoon maca powder
1 teaspoon baking powder
1 teaspoon vanilla bean powder
1 tablespoon coconut sugar
2 large eggs, whisked
100 g raw chocolate, roughly
    chopped

**COCONUT COOKIE
DOUGH CRUMBLE**
5 large (110 g) fresh medjool
    dates, pitted and roughly
    chopped
2 tablespoons cashew butter
1 tablespoon tahini
1 tablespoon coconut oil
25 g (½ cup) flaked coconut

1   Preheat the oven to 160°C (140°C fan-forced). Line the base and sides of a 20 cm square cake tin with non-stick baking paper.

2   Make the coconut cookie dough first by processing the dates, cashew butter, tahini and coconut oil in a small food processor until the mixture comes together in a ball. Add the flaked coconut and pulse together a few times until the coconut is just combined with the dough but not too broken up.

3   Place the cacao butter, almond meal, powders, sugar and eggs in a large bowl and mix until well combined, then fold through the chocolate. Spread this mixture evenly over the base of the prepared tin. Drop macadamia-sized pieces of the coconut-cookie dough over the surface of the mixture, pressing them into the batter lightly.

4   Bake for 30 minutes, or until firm around the edges and golden and just set in the centre. Cool completely in the tin, then cut into squares. Serve right away, or transfer to an airtight container in the fridge for up to 1 week.

# Vegan lemon and blueberry cheesecake

**GF**    **DF**    **VEG**    **VEGAN**

**SERVES** 12
**PREP** 25 MINUTES
+ OVERNIGHT SOAKING
+ 3 HOURS FREEZING

---

**BASE**
200 g (1¼ cups) whole natural
    almonds
6 large fresh medjool dates,
    pitted and roughly chopped
1 teaspoon vanilla bean powder
½ teaspoon ground cinnamon

**LEMON AND
BLUEBERRY FILLING**
280 g (2 cups) raw cashews,
    soaked overnight in water,
    then drained well
125 ml (½ cup) melted coconut
    oil
zest and juice of 2 large lemons
2 tablespoons pure maple syrup
300 g fresh blueberries

1    Line the base and sides of a 20 cm square cake tin with non-stick baking paper, making sure to allow overhang on two sides (this will help you remove the cheesecake from the tin later).

2    Pulse all the ingredients for the cheesecake base in a food processor until everything is very finely chopped and the mixture starts to form a ball (you may need to add 1–2 tablespoons of water to help the mixture along). Transfer to the prepared tin and press out firmly and evenly to completely cover the base.

3    Place the drained cashews, coconut oil, lemon zest and juice and maple syrup in a clean food processor and mix for 2–3 minutes, or until completely smooth and creamy. Pour into the cake tin and level the surface with a palette knife. Scatter the blueberries over the top and press them lightly into the mixture.

4    Freeze for 2–3 hours, or until just firmly set. Using the overhanging baking paper, carefully lift the cheesecake out of the tin and onto a serving plate. Cut into 12 pieces and serve immediately (see note).

## Note

This is a great dessert to make ahead of time. You can store it in an airtight container in the freezer for up to 3 months. Place in the fridge for 1 hour before serving to soften slightly. And if you have any leftovers, feel free to pop those back in the freezer too!

*Indulge moderately, without guilt!*

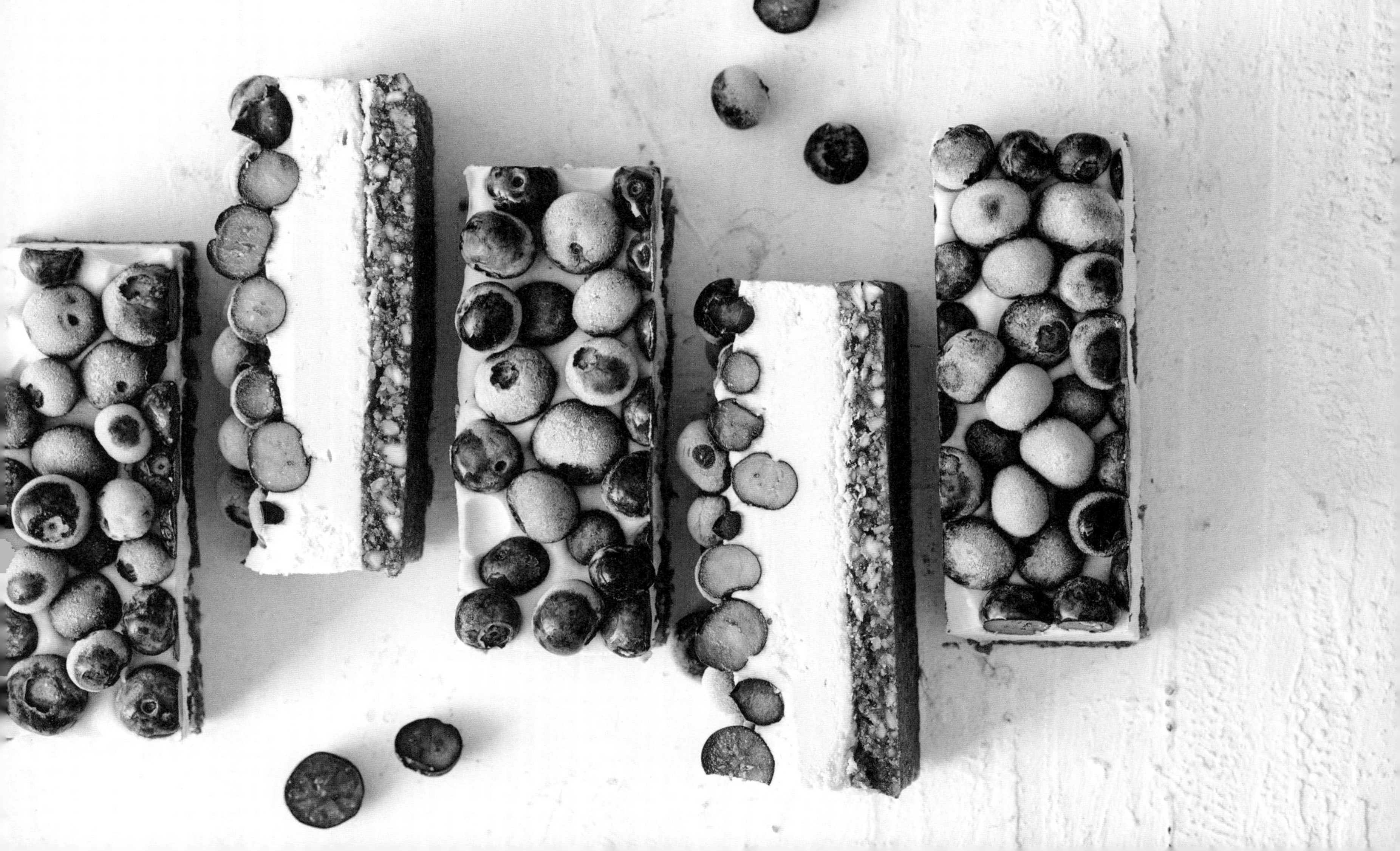

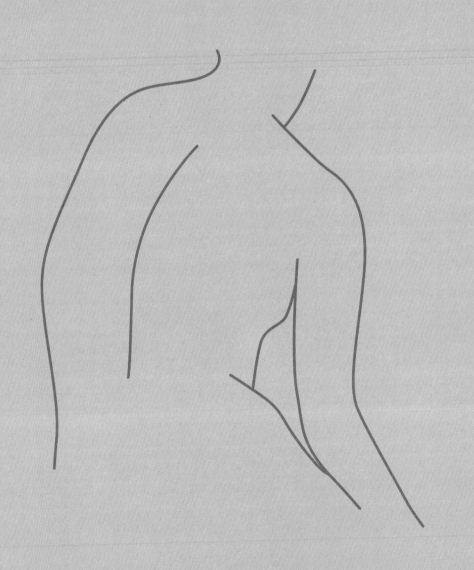

# 12

# Finally, remember that there are no rules

---

*'The healthy life does not mean the perfect life.' This reminds me that to be truly healthy, we need to be flexible and commited to balance. It took me a long time to learn this. It's so freeing!*

# My dieting days

I remember the days when I'd wake up at 6 am for a spin class, and then make a perfectly measured low-calorie breakfast. If I poured more than 30 grams into my bowl, I'd tip some out for fear of breaking my diet.

The same thing would happen at lunch and dinner. If my lunch was in any way 'imperfect', I'd squeeze in an extra high-intensity workout in the afternoon. Now that I think about it, I exercised twice a day most days to meet this idea of perfection in my mind. And if I missed a workout, the guilt would consume me for the rest of the day.

My obsessive eating didn't go unnoticed. When I was eighteen, I was at a Japanese restaurant with my family celebrating my grandfather's birthday. I was in the diet trap, and the very definition of an orthorexic – I was scared of even slightly steering away from my 'healthy routine'. When you're orthorexic, you need to be in control of your eating choices. And if you don't follow your diet perfectly, you feel like you've lost control of all aspects of your life.

So I sat there, picking apart the menu; it felt like none of the options lined up with my healthy-eating plan. I turned to my mum and said, 'I can't eat anything here, so I'm just not going to order food.' Obviously, Japanese is a fairly healthy cuisine, and there were tons of dishes I could have chosen – but I was so stuck on my idea of perfection that I needed my salad with tuna and low-fat dressing. Nothing else would suffice.

Mum stood up and said, 'Jess, come with me.' We walked outside and she told me sternly, 'You are ordering food. Whether you like it or not, you will be eating something here. I'll get you the salmon and rice.'

I can't describe the fear that ran through my body at the thought of eating food I hadn't planned to eat. Mum could clearly see the dangerous path I was heading down – how could she not? I wasn't hiding it. Soon after this, she sent me to a nutritionist and put me into therapy to deal with my disordered eating, which was getting worse by the day.

**I wasn't happy living this way.** *Not at all.*

# The rise of orthorexia

Orthorexia is an obsessive way of eating that involves only eating foods that one deems healthy. Think of it as taking health to the extreme. Orthorexia is the fear of eating anything except clean, healthy foods. Thanks to social media and the amount of (often conflicting) information available to us, many young people I meet suffer from orthorexia.

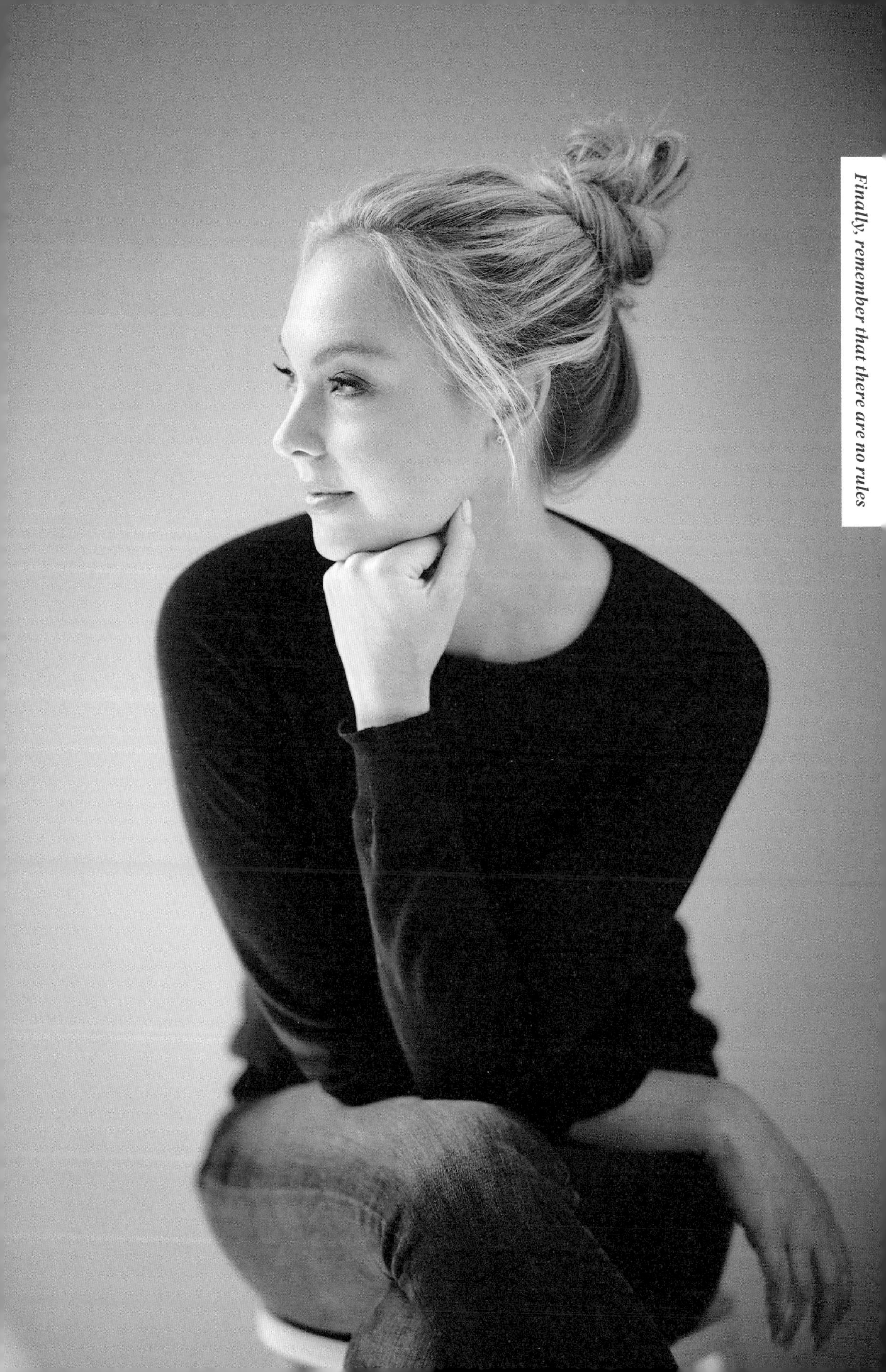

I used to be one of them, so I recognise the signs. It's a trap that's so easy to fall into. Obsessive behaviours around food start to form, someone starts being too careful about what they eat, and they end up scared to eat anything but 'clean' food. The problem is that this adds huge physical and emotional stress to the body and mind. It can also cause disordered eating.

Food is fuel and nourishment – that's all! When it comes to healthy eating and being too restrictive with a healthy-eating plan, the lines are very blurry. For me, the red flag was when I started to feel anxiety around food in social settings – like that night at the Japanese restaurant.

## How do you know if you're suffering?

You know something is an issue when it starts to dominate your thoughts. Do you think about your last meal hours after you've eaten it? Or wake up worried about what you ate the night before? If so, it's a good idea to find support to help you come out of this headspace. As a nutritionist, I'm passionate about helping women to get out of this cycle and find balance.

If you're obsessed with being healthy, please work through these steps.

- See a therapist who specialises in eating disorders as soon as you can. Your doctor should be able to recommend someone. And don't feel ashamed or afraid – we all need help sometimes.
- Put the tips and strategies I've suggested in this book into action to help you to develop a gentle relationship with food and your body.
- Aim to eat well most of the time, and indulge twice a week. This is so healthy for the mind, body and soul. Flick back to Chapter 11 for tips on indulging, as well as delicious alternatives to treats.
- Start feeling grateful for your body, and treat it with kindness and respect. You are too precious to let the pressure of perfection take over.
- Set social media boundaries. I'm bringing this up again because it's that important. We have to be careful with social media, as it can have a negative impact on our eating habits, mental health and body image. Please unfollow people who are promoting extreme diets or body shapes, and then set boundaries that suit your lifestyle. Chapter 5 can guide you through this.

Thankfully, I'm on the other side now and I couldn't imagine living with that level of self-imposed pressure. Those days of striving for perfection were dark, lonely and riddled with anxiety. I felt as though something larger than me had taken over: the disease of disordered eating. Being thin and following my routine made me feel in control, but it didn't make me happy.

**Being _anxious_ and _fearful_ about food is not good for your health.**

# Forget about perfection

There's an assumption held by many that in order to be healthy, we have to be perfect. We must eat perfectly, abide by every health rule perfectly and exercise perfectly ... The list goes on. But this mentality is the furthest thing from healthy. The pressure and anxiety that come with trying to do everything 'perfectly' chips away at everyday happiness and self-worth, to the point where it becomes hard to find balance or peace. It also makes it very difficult to achieve body love. The pressure just builds and builds.

Perfection is toxic for the mind, body and soul. It's time to let it go.

You can let go of perfection and STILL achieve your health goals.

Please don't think that the healthy life means doing it all right, all the time. I'm here to tell you that it doesn't have to be that way. In fact, it shouldn't be that way.

The title of this chapter is completely true for me. When it comes to living a healthy life, I believe in a kind, flexible and balanced approach. I don't force myself to follow rules.

> And *I don't want you* to feel like you have to stick to the rules, either.

Because there are no rules!

# Do what feels good for you

Now, I'm guided by what makes me feel good. That's why I eat well most of the time, move my body as much as I can and take steps to reduce my stress. I feel better when I do these things. It's as simple as that.

When we feel good, we have the confidence and energy to make healthy choices, and we wake up feeling like the best version of ourselves.

In this book, I've shared gentle guidelines and tools that will help you to feel good – both physically and mentally. They work for me and I know they will work for you, if you can commit to making a change.

It all begins with being kind to yourself. This is the foundation of the healthy life – a life you will want to sustain forever. Kindness is a form of self-love, self-respect and self-care. As I said in Chapter 2, I believe that kindness is the most transformational tool you can take away from *The 12-Step Mind-Body-Food Reset*.

If you can be kind to yourself, every decision you make will come from a place of self-care, not self-punishment. If you can forget the rigid rules and focus instead on doing what feels good, you'll be free. If you can let go of the pressure of perfection, you'll create the space you need to heal, change and transform.

# Your body is strong. Trust it to do its job

Your new goal is to tune in to your appetite and feed your body the fuel it needs. Ultimately, it needs to eat beautiful, natural wholefoods most of the time. But sometimes, that doesn't happen, and that's okay.

If you're travelling, or don't have access to healthy choices, be kind to yourself and just do your best with the options available to you. If you make a 'bad' food choice, please forgive yourself right away. If you're too tired to exercise, give yourself permission to rest. Don't beat yourself up, and don't throw in the towel.

Be flexible and aim for balance, not perfection. Remember, your body is an amazing machine. It's so strong, and it can handle the odd indulgence. This balanced approach to eating puts the body at ease.

*Small* changes = *big* changes

The healthy life is about steady progress and small/manageable changes that last. The healthy life is about forming a kinder and more wholesome relationship with food and your body. The healthy life is about eating healthily most of the time but allowing yourself enough leeway for indulgence, flexibility with food, imperfect choices, a social life and just LIVING. When you love your body, you want to take care of it.

# You can eat the healthy way, no matter where you go

As you now know, I don't believe in following a regimented meal plan. I believe in being flexible with food. It's so freeing knowing I can eat in a healthy way, no matter where I am.

My advice: follow the nutritional principles I outlined in Chapter 3. That way, you'll nourish your body and also be able to give yourself permission to veer away from that a couple of times a week. Go back to Chapter 11 for more about my indulgence philosophy.

### Eat with joy

Eating is such a simple pleasure, and I love the rituals connected to it: catching up with your family and friends over a meal, celebrating a special occasion at a restaurant and sharing delicious dishes is so great! Let's eat with joy, not guilt. Flick back to Chapter 5 for a refresher on how to eat mindfully and practise positive thoughts and affirmations at mealtimes.

# I'm here to support you

My business came about by accident, for which I'm truly grateful.

I felt so alone with my struggles and when I began to heal, I wanted to start a conversation, in case other women were feeling lost and alone too. So I created a blog – and somehow, it got attention. Honestly, I think it was because I was having real conversations that women were craving. It's become a platform that supports women in blocking out the noise of the diet culture, and ditching the extreme behaviours and mentalities around health. It's been there to listen and watch as they learn to let go of the pursuit of perfection, be flexible with food – and, above all, to be kind to themselves. It's proven that a balanced approach can work – and it's the best way to live the healthy life.

As a result, the women in my community have never felt better. Finally, they have a healthy relationship with food and their bodies. Finally, they feel good enough. Every story I hear and every message I receive brings tears to my eyes. I truly feel like this is my reason for being on this earth. Please share your stories with me.

## This unexpected ride has helped me too

JSHealth is truly my biggest blessing. This journey has taught me to be vulnerable. It opened my heart, challenged my deepest fears and softened my inner critic. It brought me closer to myself again – and I'm not exaggerating when I say that I lost myself for a long time.

It has helped me to forgive myself, and stop with the comparisons. It has encouraged me to be kind, but strong. It has given me the freedom to live my best life and treasure the body I live in.

It has allowed me to connect with like-minded women, for whom I have so much love and respect. They are strong, brave and beautifully open.

*You* **are my biggest inspiration.**

Popular culture and social media may have told you over and over again that you're not enough – maybe you even started to believe it was true. But I hope that this book has guided you to realise that you are enough, you are beautiful, and that perfection doesn't exist.

I know what it's like to battle with your body day in, day out. I know how difficult and daunting the healthy life can be.

You're not alone. My 12 steps prove that the healthy life doesn't need to be complicated; it's simple and based on self-love. This is a lifestyle you can continue forever – and it's a lifestyle you will want to continue forever.

I'm here to support you through this realistic and sustainable way of life.

You deserve freedom. You deserve to wake up and feel GOOD. Every single day. Cheers to that!

*(p.s. It is worth copying!)*

# YOUR DAILY PLANNER: LESS STRESS, MORE REST!

Before we wrap things up, let's run through what a day in your new balanced life might look like. Think of this as your daily checklist for a healthy life, mind and body! If it's a prep day, spend an hour making some delicious food for the week ahead.

## First thing in the morning

1. Think of 3–5 things you're grateful for.
2. If you have time, enjoy a 10-minute meditation or deep belly breathing session.
3. Enjoy a big glass of warm water with a squeeze of lemon and a pinch of salt. Pop your daily probiotic for good gut health and immune support.

This positive wake-up sets the tone for the day ahead. Remember to avoid all social media to alleviate any anxiety.

## Pre-breakfast

If coffee is your thing, sip on one before 10 am (either before your workout or after breakfast). Optional pre-workout snack: An apple, banana, berries or healthy energy bar.

## Workout

Exercise for 30 minutes in a way you love. This could be running, walking, yoga, Pilates or HIIT. Be kind, gentle and moderate – no need to overdo it. If you're short on time or too tired to exercise, meditate or go for a walk after dinner.

## Breakfast

Enjoy a balanced, nutrient-dense breakfast (see Chapter 4). Include a portion of protein, fibre and good fats, and avoid high-sugar and high-carb options. Sit down to eat, and don't eat while you're on the move. Pop your daily vitamins, as guided by a health practitioner.

## Morning snack

Eat a small snack to stabilise your blood sugars and tide you over until lunch.

## Lunch

Enjoy a healthy lunch. Preferably one you've made yourself! Think quick, easy, and satiating. Plate up your food and take three deep breaths to calm your digestion before eating.

## Have a 4–5 pm snack

Savour a protein-rich snack at 4–5 pm. This reduces overeating, sugar cravings and bingeing in the evenings. Chapter 9 has heaps of good options.

## The Stress-Free Zone

When you get home from work, go into the SFZ for 10–20 minutes. Do something that makes you happy and calm, such as walking in the park, reading a book, watching a TV show, meditating or (my favourite stress-buster) lying down with your legs up against a wall for 10 minutes. Remember to avoid phones and social media at this time.

## Dinner

Whip up a quick and easy nutritious dinner (check out Chapter 8 for ideas and recipes), then eat it slowly and mindfully. And without your phone! But you know that by now.

## Post-dinner rituals

- If you haven't had time to exercise already, go for a 10–20-minute stroll or work through a few yoga poses.
- Switch off all social media, phones and emails by 8–9 pm. Choose a time that works with your lifestyle. Put your phone in another room.
- Enjoy a cup of caffeine-free tea with warm almond milk and cinnamon, and savour a healthy sweet treat, if you wish. This will kick any late-night cravings for refined sugar.
- Take magnesium glycinate for good sleep, as guided by a health practitioner.
- Soak in an epsom salt bath with lavender oil three times a week.
- Put your legs up against the wall for 10 minutes and breathe deeply. This will help you to fall asleep faster.
- Tuck yourself into bed by 10.30 pm, and aim for between 7 and 9 hours of sleep.

## Do this, and you'll feel AMAZING!

# Nutrition guide

For a lean, healthy and energetic body, work on fuelling your body with wholefoods. This nutrition guide outlines the foods to eat, and also the foods to avoid as much as possible – because you will just feel better doing this! It also includes serving sizes.

The JSHealth philosophy is about balance and no extremes. I believe in eating everything in moderation, so just steer clear of those foods to avoid most of the time.

## Carbohydrates

Carbs are essential for your energy and overall health – you don't need to ban them from your kitchen. Just choose the right kinds! If you're suffering from low energy or digestive problems, try cutting out gluten for 2–4 weeks.

### ✓ Carbs to enjoy

| *Wholegrains* | *Gluten-free grains* | *Other GF alternatives* |
|---|---|---|
| – slice rye, sourdough or spelt bread<br>– 1–2 mountain bread or wholegrain Lebanese wraps<br>– 1 thin slice pumpernickel or ezekiel bread<br>– ½ cup uncooked rolled oats<br>– ¼ cup uncooked oat bran<br>– 2 Ryvitas | – ½ cup uncooked quinoa<br>– ½ cup uncooked brown or wild rice<br>– ½ cup uncooked brown rice pasta<br>– ½ cup uncooked millet<br>– ½ cup uncooked amaranth<br>– ½ cup uncooked buckwheat<br>– 1 cup cooked gluten-free noodles: buckwheat, kelp, konjac, mung bean and black bean, brown rice, pulse<br>– 3–4 corn thins | – 3–4 flaxseed buckwheat crackers<br>– ½ cup uncooked gluten-free oats<br>– 1–2 slices homemade gluten-free bread<br>– 2 brown rice cakes |

## ✗ Carbs to avoid or reduce

- White/refined carbohydrates, such as bread, pasta, rice, pita bread, crackers
- Other refined wheat products, such as noodles, cookies, cakes, pies, waffles
- Gluten-free products made with corn flour, rice starch or potato starch
- Chips/crisps
- Packaged breakfast cereals – they're full of sugar!

# Fruit and veg

Buy fresh, seasonal and organic fruit and vegetables when you can. I encourage you to enjoy fruit with your breakfast or as a mid-morning snack, and avoid it in the afternoon – it can affect your blood sugar balance and sleep.

## ✓ Fruits to enjoy

### Low-GI fruits

- 1 apple
- ½ cup berries e.g. strawberries, blueberries or raspberries
- ¼ cup goji berries
- 1–2 figs
- 1 citrus fruit e.g. lemons, grapefruit or oranges)
- 1 papaya
- 2–3 kiwifruit
- 2–3 passionfruit
- 1–2 stone fruit e.g. nectarines, plums or peaches

### High-sugar fruits (Eat moderately)

- 2 dates
- 1 small banana
- 1 small mango
- 1 small bunch of grapes
- 1–2 wedges watermelon
- 6–8 cherries
- 6–8 lychees

## ✗ Fruits to avoid

- Dried fruits e.g. apricots, sultanas
- Tinned and stewed fruits (unless they're homemade)

## √ Vegetables to enjoy

### Non-starchy veg

### Starchy veg

Try to include at least 2 cups of veggies in every meal.

½ cup per meal

- Dark leafy greens e.g. silverbeet, bok choy or kale (unlimited)
- Asparagus
- Brassica veggies e.g. brussels sprouts, broccoli, cauliflower, cabbage, kale (cooked)
- Capsicum/red peppers
- All lettuces
- Rocket
- Mushrooms
- Onions, garlic and leek
- Radish
- Celery
- Zucchini
- Cucumber
- Carrots
- Fennel
- Tomatoes
- Green beans
- Eggplant
- Seaweed

- Sweet potato
- Pumpkin
- Beetroot
- Parsnip
- Peas
- Corn
- Potato

**No veggies to avoid!**

# Beans and legumes

These are a source of both carbohydrates and protein, and they're high in fibre.

## √ Beans and legumes to enjoy

- Black beans
- Kidney beans
- Mung beans
- Butterbeans
- Chickpeas
- Lentils
- Split peas

# Protein

Protein feeds every cell in your body, so enjoy a portion at every meal.

## √ Protein to enjoy

### Animal protein

- 2 organic free-range eggs
- 150–200 g fish: white fish such as hake, sole, barramundi and snapper, or sustainably sourced salmon
- 90–150 g twice per week max tinned or bottled tuna
- 6–8 prawns
- 100–150 g free-range organic poultry e.g. chicken, turkey or duck
- 150 g grass-fed lean red meat e.g. lamb, veal or beef

### Vegetarian protein

- 1 cup cooked legumes
- 100 g tofu (consume moderately) or tempeh
- 2–3 tablespoons hummus or tahini
- 100–200 g dairy products e.g. organic natural yoghurt, unsweetened Greek yoghurt, goat's/sheep's milk yoghurt or goat's cheese
- ¼ cup nuts and/or seeds
- 2 organic free-range eggs

### Protein powder

- 30 g whey/rice/pea protein powder

## X Proteins to avoid

- Cold deli meats
- Sausages
- Smoked meats
- 'Diet' or 'low-fat' yoghurts

- Protein powders containing gluten, GMOs, and artificial sweeteners, colours and preservatives

# Dairy

Limit dairy to two serves per day.

## ✓ Dairy to enjoy

| Cheese | Yoghurt | Other | Dairy substitutes |
|---|---|---|---|
| – 2–3 tablespoons goat's cheese/feta<br>– 2–3 tablespoons cottage cheese<br>– 3 tablespoons ricotta<br>– 2–3 tablespoons other white cheeses e.g. mozzarella | – 100–200 g natural/Greek-style yoghurt<br>– 100–200 g goat's/sheep's yoghurt | – 250 ml/1 cup per day organic or A2 cow's milk<br>– 1 teaspoon organic butter | – 250 ml/1 cup almond milk<br>– 250 ml/1 cup coconut milk<br>– 100 g coconut yoghurt<br>– 30–50 g cashew cheese |

## ✗ Dairy or dairy substitutes to avoid

- Yellow cheeses
- Low-fat/'diet' yoghurt
- Yoghurt with added sugar, sweeteners and fruit
- Skim milk
- Margarine

# Soy

For some people, soy can depress thyroid function, impact hormones and slow down digestion. If you have an underactive thyroid, reduce soy products, including fermented ones. If you don't have any thyroid issues, you can enjoy fermented soy products, such as miso, tempeh, tamari (in moderate amounts). But avoid tofu and soy milk.

# Good fats

These are vital for good health and wellbeing, and they promote healthy skin. Enjoy in moderation.

## √ Good fats to enjoy

- ¼–½ avocado
- 1 tablespoon cold-pressed extra-virgin olive oil, virgin organic coconut oil, flaxseed oil
- ¼ cup mixed nuts and seeds
- 1 tablespoon organic nut butter
- 1–2 tablespoons tahini
- butter

## X Fats to avoid

X Trans fats such as those found in vegetable oil, margarine, processed and packaged foods, fried foods
X Commercial peanut butter with added sugar

# Nuts and seeds

Nuts and seeds are high in essential vitamins and minerals. They're also a good source of fatty acids and protein.

## √ Nuts and seeds to enjoy

¼–½ cup max per day, unroasted and unsalted

- Almonds
- Cashews
- Walnuts
- Pecans
- Macadamias
- Hazelnuts
- Brazil nuts
- Sesame seeds
- Sunflower seeds
- Pepitas

**No nuts and seeds to avoid!**

# Sauces, oils and condiments

Use these healthy condiments to jazz up your meals instead of bottled sauces or dressings.

## ✓ Sauces and condiments to enjoy

1–2 tablespoons per serve

- Vinegars e.g. apple cider vinegar, white wine vinegar, balsamic vinegar
- Cold-pressed extra-virgin olive oil or sesame oil (for cooking over medium heats)
- Virgin organic coconut oil or ghee (good for cooking over high heats)
- Salads: olive oil or flaxseed oil
- Dijon or wholegrain mustard
- Tamari
- Tahini/hummus
- Lemon/lime juice
- Homemade guacamole
- Homemade pesto
- Homemade tomato sauce
- Tomato paste or Napoletana sauce

## ✗ Sauces, oils and condiments to avoid

- Commercial condiments e.g. bottled salad dressings, tomato or barbecue sauce, relish, chutney and packaged gravy
- Vegetable oils e.g. sunflower oil, safflower oil, canola oil, margarine

# Healthy flours

If you love baking as much as I do, gravitate towards these flours.

## ✓ Flours to enjoy

- Buckwheat flour
- Coconut flour
- Almond meal
- Oat flour
- Spelt flour
- Arrowroot flour

## ✗ Flours to avoid

- White wheat flours

# Herbs and spices

Herbs and spices add flavour and nutrition to meals.

## √ Herbs and spices to enjoy

### Herbs and spices (dry/fresh)

To taste

- Coriander
- Mint
- Parsley
- Basil
- Sumac
- Chives
- Oregano
- Rosemary
- Sage
- Thyme
- Garlic
- Ginger
- Turmeric
- Cayenne pepper
- Chilli flakes
- Za'atar
- Paprika
- Cumin (seeds or ground)
- Ground cinnamon
- Fennel (seeds or ground)

### Salts

No more than
1 teaspoon per day

- Himalayan salt
- Celtic sea salt
- Herb salt

## X Herbs and spices to avoid

X Table salt
X Herbs and spices with added salt or sugar (check the nutrition label)

# Sweeteners

Steer clear of refined sugar and artificial sweeteners, and sweeten your food the natural way.

## ✓ Natural sweeteners to enjoy

| *Natural sweeteners* | *Sugar alternatives* These support blood sugar balance |
|---|---|
| Limit to 1–2 teaspoons per day | To taste |
| – Organic raw honey<br>– Pure maple syrup<br>– Rice malt syrup | – Stevia liquid or powder<br>– Ground cinnamon<br>– Vanilla bean/powder<br>– Grated nutmeg |

## ✗ Sweeteners to avoid or reduce

| | |
|---|---|
| – White and brown sugar<br>– Refined sugar products e.g. lollies, chocolate, ice creams, energy bars, jellies, jams | – Artificial sweeteners e.g. Equal or Splenda<br>– High-fructose corn syrup |

# Drinks

Hydration is the cornerstone of great health, so drink up!

## √ Drinks to enjoy

- 1.5–2 litres per day filtered water
- Herbal teas
- Freshly squeezed veggie juices – less fruit, more greens!
- 1 per day caffeinated drinks (including coffee, black tea and matcha)
- Coconut water
- Wholesome smoothies
- 250 ml/1 cup per day nut milks e.g. unsweetened almond/coconut milk

## X Drinks to avoid

- Soft drinks – including 'diet' versions
- Cordials
- Fruit juices
- Milkshakes/thickshakes
- Iced lattes, frappuccinos and coffees with added syrup
- Energy drinks
- Cocktails (they're full of sugar)

# A few more foods to avoid

A few more items to add to the 'limited' list.

## X And give these foods a miss too

- Pre-packaged and processed foods
- Deep-fried foods
- 'Fat-free' and low-calorie items – they're often loaded with sugar
- Artificial sweeteners
- All 'diet' foods
- Frozen meals, where possible
- Preservatives

# Coffee

The JSHealth rule is to **limit caffeine to one cup per day** (including coffee, green tea, black tea and matcha), and **drink it before 10 am.**

The problem with too much caffeine goes beyond the jitters – it can cause anxiety, sleep issues and hormonal imbalances. It can also increase your stress levels and sugar cravings, and lower your energy, liver and digestive function. Caffeine causes a rise in cortisol, which can make weight balance difficult.

So stick to one caffeinated drink per day, and make it healthier by skipping sugar, cream and sweeteners. Then savour it! I do.

## √ This is what a healthy coffee looks like

| | |
|---|---|
| Long black | Black coffee |
| Piccolo | One shot of espresso with a dash of organic cow's milk or almond milk |
| Macchiato/Americano | Black coffee with an optional dash of organic cow's milk or almond milk |
| Latte or flat white | One shot of espresso with ½–1 cup milk. Avoid added sugar and syrups. |

### *Some great coffee alternatives*
√ Herbal tea – e.g. ginger, peppermint, chamomile
√ Dandelion tea/coffee – it has the same rich, bitter taste as coffee!
√ Turmeric latte
√ Decaf/rooibos chai with hot almond milk and cinnamon

# Alcohol

I believe alcohol can be part of a healthy lifestyle – as long as it's consumed responsibly and moderately. Consider alcohol a treat, and save it for weekends and special occasions.

The JSHealth rule is no more than 2–3 drinks in one sitting. During the week, go alcohol-free. Avoid cocktails, and avoid drinks where cordials, juices or soft drinks are used as mixers, as these contain loads of sugar.

Instead, opt for wiser alcohol options, such as red wine, gin, vodka or whisky mixed with sparkling water or soda water and flavoured with fresh lemon or lime.

**Top tip:** Enjoy a small snack or meal before you start drinking.

# What about supplements?

I'm all about smart supplementing. I aim to get most of the nutrients I need from food, and then I supplement to support specific issues like gut health, energy and sleep.

**Please note:** It's important that a good health practitioner guides you when it comes to determining the right supplements and dosage for you. Never self-prescribe.

These are the supplements I take every day:

- Multi-strain probiotic. Probiotics work to rebalance your gut bacteria, and assist with constipation, energy, weight management and allergies. Take once daily in the morning, or last thing at night.
- Magnesium glycinate or citrate. My favourite magic mineral, magnesium is great for stress reduction, sleep, blood sugar balance and constipation. Take in powder or capsule form before bed.
- B complex. This supports energy, stress and thyroid health. Take with breakfast, and avoid in the afternoon as it can affect sleep.
- Multi-mineral. Look for one containing zinc, iodine and selenium to support different body systems, and boost thyroid health and energy. Take with breakfast.

I have developed a range of JSHealth vitamins that address common health concerns such as low energy, stress, sleep, bloating, sugar cravings and skin. We also have a multivitamin that is a one-a-day formula. Visit **jshealthvitamins.com** to order online.

# Notes

Page 12: 'A study of long-term dieters found that years of restricting calories reduced their metabolic rates by 13 per cent ...'; Éric T. Poehlman, January 2003, 'Reduced metabolic rate after caloric restriction: can we agree on how to normalize the data?', *Journal of Clinical Endocrinology & Metabolism*, vol. 88, issue 1, pp. 14–15, <https://doi.org/10.1210/jc.2002-021672>.

Page 12: Another study confirmed this, reporting that low-calorie dieting slowed down metabolism ...'; PA Molé, August 1990, 'Impact of energy intake and exercise on resting metabolic rate', *Journal of Sports Medicine*, vol. 10, issue 2, pp. 72–87, <https://www.ncbi.nlm.nih.gov/pubmed/2204100>.

Page 12: 'Professor of psychology Traci Mann has conducted studies on the relationship between restrictive dieting and successful weight loss ...'; Traci Mann, May 2018, American Psychological Association website, 'Why do dieters regain weight?', viewed February 2019, <https://www.apa.org/science/about/psa/2018/05/calorie-deprivation.aspx>.

Page 12: 'One study surveyed twenty dieters ...'; Samantha L. Thomas et al., November 2008, '"They all work ... when you stick to them": a qualitative investigation of dieting, weight loss and physical exercise in obese individuals', *Nutrition Journal*, vol. 7, issue 34, <https://doi.org/10.1186/1475-2891-7-34>.

Page 23: In fact, scientists have found that between one- and two-thirds of dieters actually regained more weight than they initially lost.; David Benton and Hayley A. Young, September 2017, 'Reducing calorie intake may not help you lose body weight', *Perspectives on Psychological Science*, vol. 12, issue 5, pp. 703–714, <https://doi.org/10.1177/1745691617690878>.

Page 30: 'Ego is much more than an overinflated sense of self ...'; Eckhart Tolle (as told to Leigh Newman), 10 October 2011, Oprah's Lifeclass: 'Free yourself from your ego armour', viewed February 2019, <http://www.oprah.com/oprahs-lifeclass/eckhart-tolle-on-how-to-free-yourself-from-your-ego-armor#ixzz5YYxxCp23>.

Page 178: Scientists have found a direct connection between our blood sugar levels and gut bacteria; Brenda Goodman, 9 March 2018, 'Enlisting gut bacteria and fiber to fight diabetes', WebMD website, viewed February 2019, <https://www.webmd.com/diabetes/news/20180309/enlisting-gut-bacteria-and-fiber-to-fight-diabetes>.

Page 183: A recent study found that just one night of less or broken sleep can have an effect ...; SM Schmid et al., September 2008, 'A single night of sleep deprivation increases ghrelin levels and feelings of hunger in normal-weight healthy men', *Journal of Sleep Research*, vol. 17, issue 3, pp. 331–4, <https://doi.org/10.1111/j.1365-2869.2008.00662.x>.

Page 201: A study of young women found that participants following 'acute resistance exercise' ...; KL Osterberg and CL Melby, March 2000, 'Effect of acute resistance exercise on postexercise oxygen consumption and resting metabolic rate in young women', *International Journal of Sport Nutrition and Exercise Metabolism*, vol. 10, issue 1, pp. 71–81 (Erratum in *International Journal of Sport Nutrition and Exercise Metabolism*, September 2000, vol. 10, issue 3, p. 360), <https://www.ncbi.nlm.nih.gov/pubmed/10939877>.

# Conversion chart

Measuring cups and spoons may vary slightly from one country to another, but the difference is generally not enough to affect a recipe. All cup and spoon measures are level.

One Australian metric measuring cup holds 250 ml (8 fl oz), one Australian tablespoon holds 20 ml (4 teaspoons) and one Australian metric teaspoon holds 5 ml. North America, New Zealand and the UK use a 15 ml (3-teaspoon) tablespoon.

## Length

| METRIC | IMPERIAL |
|--------|----------|
| 3 mm | ⅛ inch |
| 6 mm | ¼ inch |
| 1 cm | ½ inch |
| 2.5 cm | 1 inch |
| 5 cm | 2 inches |
| 18 cm | 7 inches |
| 20 cm | 8 inches |
| 23 cm | 9 inches |
| 25 cm | 10 inches |
| 30 cm | 12 inches |

## Liquid measures

| ONE AMERICAN PINT | ONE IMPERIAL PINT |
|-------------------|-------------------|
| 500 ml (16 fl oz) | 600 ml (20 fl oz) |

| CUP | METRIC | IMPERIAL |
|-----|--------|----------|
| ⅛ cup | 30 ml | 1 fl oz |
| ¼ cup | 60 ml | 2 fl oz |
| ⅓ cup | 80 ml | 2½ fl oz |
| ½ cup | 125 ml | 4 fl oz |
| ⅔ cup | 160 ml | 5 fl oz |
| ¾ cup | 180 ml | 6 fl oz |
| 1 cup | 250 ml | 8 fl oz |
| 2 cups | 500 ml | 16 fl oz |
| 2¼ cups | 560 ml | 20 fl oz |
| 4 cups | 1 litre | 32 fl oz |

## Dry measures

The most accurate way to measure dry ingredients is to weigh them. However, if using a cup, add the ingredient loosely to the cup and level with a knife; don't compact the ingredient unless the recipe requests 'firmly packed'.

| METRIC | IMPERIAL |
|--------|----------|
| 15 g | ½ oz |
| 30 g | 1 oz |
| 60 g | 2 oz |
| 125 g | 4 oz (¼ lb) |
| 185 g | 6 oz |
| 250 g | 8 oz (½ lb) |
| 375 g | 12 oz (¾ lb) |
| 500 g | 16 oz (1 lb) |
| 1 kg | 32 oz (2 lb) |

## Oven temperatures

| CELSIUS | FAHRENHEIT |
|---------|------------|
| 100°C | 200°F |
| 120°C | 250°F |
| 150°C | 300°F |
| 160°C | 325°F |
| 180°C | 350°F |
| 200°C | 400°F |
| 220°C | 425°F |

| CELSIUS | GAS MARK |
|---------|----------|
| 110°C | ¼ |
| 130°C | ½ |
| 140°C | 1 |
| 150°C | 2 |
| 170°C | 3 |
| 180°C | 4 |
| 190°C | 5 |
| 200°C | 6 |
| 220°C | 7 |
| 230°C | 8 |
| 240°C | 9 |
| 250°C | 10 |

# Index

# Thank you

This book could only have happened with the love and support I have received from the incredible people in my life.

A very heartfelt thankyou to: Dean, my darling husband. Thank you for your unconditional support during my writing of this book while we were living in Los Angeles. Your love and care has given me the strength to be brave enough to be honest about my journey and write this book. I love you so much.

Nicky, my biggest cooking inspiration. You taught me almost everything that I know when it comes to how to cook with ease and joy. I will forever be grateful for passing on your knowledge and touch.

Glenn, my father. Thank you for teaching me kindness and hard work. You are the most incredible role model a daughter could have. Thank you for everything.

Gabriella and Olivia, my beautiful sisters. Thank you for the constant love, support and encouragement. I'm proud of you both.

My mother- and father-in-law, Noreen and Colin Steingold. Thank you for your unconditional love and support that you show Dean and me on a day to day basis.

Ingrid, my darling publisher. You are responsible for the launch and success of my career. It has been an honour to work with you. Your belief in me and my message means everything to me. It was the biggest compliment when you asked me to start writing a third book. I have such admiration for you, both personally and professionally.

Danielle Walker, my editor. I am so grateful for your incredible eye and hard work with this book. Without you, this book could never have come to life. It has been such a pleasure going through another labour of love with you. Thank you for being so kind and patient during this process.

Thank you to the shoot team – photographer Jeremy Simons, stylist Vanessa Austin, cook Kerrie Ray and Naomi van Groll – for bringing their A game and making this book look the best it can be. And thank you to Jacqui Porter at Northwood Green for bringing it all together with her exceptional design skills.

Katia Lervasi, JSHealth editor. I honestly do not know how we pulled this off together with such a short timeframe to work with. I could not have done it without you – that I know for sure. Your brilliant editing skills and support go me through this. Thank you for all these years of brilliant work.

JSHealth Team, you are my girls! I do not know of a more supportive team in the world. Thank you for holding everything together for me during the writing of this book. You have built JSHealth into something that I couldn't have dreamt of. Thank you.

*Jess* xo

# About the author

Jessica Sepel (BHlth, Adv Dip Nutritional Medicine) is a clinical nutritionist, author and international health and travel expert. She is also the beloved voice behind JSHealth, passionately advocating how to achieve a balanced lifestyle through wholefoods and a healthy relationship with food to her vibrant social media community on Instagram, Facebook and Youtube. She is also the founder of JSHealth Vitamins and the JSHealth App. Jess is also a regular contributor to Vogue Australia's *Spy Style*, *Well+Good NYC*, *PopSugar* and *MindBodyGreen* and brand ambassador for CottonOn and Nature's Way. Jess's first two books are *The Healthy Life* and *Living the Healthy Life*.

First published 2019 in Macmillan
by Pan Macmillan Australia Pty Limited
Level 25, 1 Market Street, Sydney, New South Wales
Australia 2000

A CIP catalogue record for this book is available from the
National Library of Australia: http://catalogue.nla.gov.au

Design by Northwood Green
Recipe development by Tracey Pattison
Edited by Katie Bosher
Index by Helena Holmgren
Prop and food styling by Vanessa Austin
Food preparation by Kerrie Ray
Hair and makeup by Paul Bedggood
Colour + reproduction by Splitting Image Colour Studio
Printed in China by 1010 Printing International Limited

10 9 8 7 6 5 4 3 2 1